The Storr, Sk

SKYE is a place I return to time and
and the Storr never looks any less s
become iconic and the summit of the
takes away the majesty of the scene a

Overlooking the Sound of Raasay o
a great place for the active to tackle the summit and the less-so to wander the Sanctuary, the area just in front of the Storr which includes the towering Old Man of Storr, soaking up the atmosphere of a truly remarkable and unique place.

Contents

Complete Stories

p121

Best Of British

p25

Poetry To Warm Your Heart

p77

Dear Readers . . .

IT gives me great pleasure to welcome you to "The People's Friend" Annual 2012! We've really enjoyed putting this one together – from selecting the very best stories and poetry to deciding which of our favourite J. Campbell Kerr cover paintings to include.

Inside, you'll find your "People's Friend" annual packed with all the things we know you love, including evocative poetry and brand-new stories to take you all through the year.

We're celebrating British wildlife, too, with our "Best Of British" series, which you'll find scattered throughout. I was absolutely fascinated to learn some facts I hadn't known about some of the UK's best-loved creatures.

So please sit back, relax, and spend some quality time with "The People's Friend" Annual 2012 – I hope you gain as much enjoyment from reading it as we have from compiling it!

Your Editor

J. Campbell Kerr Paintings

p29

Burning The Bush

by Pauline Kelly.

NOT much went on in Bredwardine. Nestling in the shadow of the mountains, the village straggled haphazardly downwards to the river and upwards to the square-towered church on its grassy knoll. It was here Jemima Threadgold came across Seth Hollybone one day as she gathered kindling.

"Hello," she said, fixing him with a curious gaze. "You look at a loose end."

"Well . . ." Seth was hesitant and Jemima waited. Whilst his brothers were tall, dark and confident, Seth was of average height, mousy-haired and quiet, with dreaming grey eyes and a liking for poetry.

"You know the tradition we have hereabouts to bring in the New Year?"

Jemima nodded. Burning the Bush was a time-honoured custom at Bredwardine. A collection of globes of hawthorn and mistletoe, hanging for the past twelve months in farmhouse kitchens, was burned on a ritual fire before dawn on New Year's morning, and while the fire was burning, new globes were fashioned. The privilege of making one fell always to a family member.

"We draw straws at home," Seth said dolefully. "This time it's fallen to me."

"You don't look too happy about it."

"I'm no good at that sort of thing. I'm no good at anything much."

"Oh, you must be. Everyone is good at something."

"Not I. Not on the farm — and that's what counts at our place."

"You're the last, like me, except we're all girls in our family. Nobody takes you seriously when you're the youngest." Jemima considered. "Making a globe isn't that hard, though, Seth. I'll show you, if you like?"

Illustration by David Axtell.

"Would you?"

"Of course. No time like the present. If we start now, you can get some practice in. Come New Year you'll be an expert."

"Let's hope you like a challenge," Seth said.

"Oh, I do," Jemima replied, smiling.

WHO'S got an admirer, then?" Liddy Threadgold said.

"You're a dark horse," Anna, her twin, put in. Jane and Maria looked on, ears flapping. "Meeting a lad on the riverside and never letting on."

"There's nothing to tell, that's why. I just bumped into Seth."

"Deaf to the world, they were," Liddy persisted. "I walked right past."

"It'll be wedding bells next. Fancy our Jemima beating us all to it!"

"It was nothing," Jemima insisted. "If I wanted an admirer it wouldn't be a Hollybone. They think too much of themselves by far!"

The moment the words were out it struck her that they didn't apply to Seth. Quiet and unassuming, he hadn't been able to thank her enough for her offer. There was something very likeable about him. The thought of seeing him again brought a frisson of pleasure and another feeling, one she couldn't quite put a name to. Still, it was too late to climb down.

"Me, walk out with Seth Hollybone?" she went on. "Don't be silly!"

And, snatching up a bedtime candle, she ran up the stairs to the attic bedroom she shared with her sisters. Tease, tease, tease! How she disliked being the youngest. Not that she couldn't take a joke. Jemima was always ready for some fun — but enough was enough.

Seth, it seemed, had to put up with the same.

"Our Abel's the worst," he said as she showed him how to twist the prickly hawthorn into shape. "The moment I drew the winning straw he was at it. I once made a shepherd's crook that didn't last the season out. I never heard the end of it and Abel had to bring the matter up again."

"Oh, dear."

Jemima's lips twitched; a slow smile of response spread over Seth's face.

"I tell you, I'm useless. Any globe I make won't last two minutes."

"Yes, it will. You might need more than one lesson, though . . ."

Getting away was not easy for Seth, and so they had arranged a sign. He would leave a red kerchief in the fork of the oak tree by the farm entrance. They'd meet here, away from prying eyes. It was unfortunate that today her sister, who worked for the village laundry-woman, had taken a short cut through the churchyard on her way to deliver some washing to a customer.

Blowing out the candle, Jemima settled down to sleep. As she drifted off she thought about Seth and the way she had warmed to his smile.

* * * *

"What's this, Seth?" Abel said, striding into the barn where Seth was privately putting in some practice. "A cage for a canary?"

"Nothing." Seth bundled the item out of sight.

"It's a hawthorn globe! You're doing a trial run so you won't make a muff of it come New Year."

It was a matter of pride. Seth knew what they all thought of him, especially Pa. Seth wanted to prove he was as good as them and what better way was there?

Abel shrugged.

"Pa's doing the farm accounts and you know what a time he has with them. He says you did it last time."

"That's right. I totalled the figures and Pa entered them in the ledger."

"He wants you to do the lot now."

"When does it have to be in?"

"Tomorrow. It's short notice, but you know how Pa puts these things off. He said we'll see to your outside work for now." Abel broke off, his gaze sliding over his young brother, then added grudgingly, "I dunno. Reckoning, penning, always a nose in book — seems you're a bit of a scholar, our Seth."

"Yes, well, happen I take after Mam's side. One of us is bound to."

"You could be right. Don't think I'd be any use at accounting."

Seth thought of Jemima saying how we were all good at something and smiled inwardly. He'd wanted to ask her out but chances were she'd think him an embarrassment, the way his family did.

"I'll go and do those books," he said. "Looks like I'm in for a late night."

THERE was no mistaking the relief on the face of Hanmer Jones, a townsman with a horror of all things rural, to find, instead of his usual blunt and burly client, the quiet-spoken figure of the youngest son.

With slight trepidation the ledger was opened, and the man visibly brightened. In place of the usual crossings out and smudges, not to mention the box of crumpled bills of sales and other paperwork, his gaze rested on pristine pages with neat columns of correctly totalled figures.

"Well, it's to be hoped you've taken over the business side of things for good, young fellow. It would make my life easier. Come to think of it, there are farmers in the neighbourhood who'd pay to have their books done . . ."

Seth could think of nothing better.

"If Pa's in agreement, sir, I wouldn't mind at all."

"Then leave it with me," Hanmer Jones said.

The upshot of it all was a rearrangement of staffing at Little Acre. Seth took over the office side, not only of their farm but others, too.

"It beats outdoor work any day," he said to Jemima. They were friends by now, in each other's confidence. "Funny thing, it never occurred to me what a bind folk find in totting up a few figures.

"It's not a bad swap at all, sitting by a fire instead of slaving out of doors. I get fed into the bargain."

It was the end of November now, the wind blowing chill off the mountains. But whatever the weather, Seth made time for Jemima. She was in his thoughts by day and his dreams at night. On his solitary rides to the outlying farms and holdings he would fantasise over the two of them setting up home together. With her deftness of hand their hearth would be a joy to come home to . . .

Jemima had once confided a long-held wish to open a shop of her own, a haberdashers where ladies of the town and countrywomen alike could purchase the headwear of their choice.

And why not? Seth could do the paperwork for his wife, as well, couldn't he? His wife. How Seth wished it were so. He looked at her longingly, trying to frame the words he so wanted to say.

In the next breath Jemima pointed to the bundle of hawthorn she had picked on her way here.

"We'd best get on. You're improving, Seth, but you've still a way to go."

"I'll do it, Jemima," Seth said resolutely.

She could see a change in Seth, Jemima thought, walking home, her shawl knotted around her against the cold. Fear fluttered through her, fear that he was growing away from her. Both Liddy and Anna were walking out now; dates were set for the weddings. Jane and Maria had gone into service. The cottage was emptying, but what of her? Would Mam expect her to stay at home and look after her and Father in their dotage?

"It's no use crossing bridges before you come to them," her mother said, when Jemima tentatively brought up the subject. "It's to be hoped we can see after ourselves for a while yet."

"But, Mam, what's to become of me?" Jemima asked.

"Why, you're growing up as pretty as a girl could wish. There's a lad somewhere who'll come calling and that'll be that."

Jemima was silent. There was only one she wanted. And he was edging further away every day. Wasn't that just the way of the world!

* * * *

December came in with frosts and Christmas brought flurries of snow.

"It's to be hoped it keeps off for the celebrations," Farmer Hollybone said, eyeing the globe that hung from a beam over the kitchen fireplace. The berries were long gone, the leaves shrivelled and brown. But the framework, expertly woven, was still intact. The farmer's gaze went to his youngest and he gave his head a shake. Seth, the odd one out. Could he rise to this all-important occasion?

On the summit of the highest hill, a great bonfire was taking shape. A fair bit of brashing had been done in the forest and there was plenty of spare timber. Much of it was divided amongst the elderly and the infirm for firewood; the rest went on the bonfire.

In every farmstead and kitchen, women were pounding and cooking, turning out pies and sweetmeats by the score. There was a side of beef big enough to feed an army and many a bird; whatever folk had to spare, they gave.

Village maids titivated a gown for the occasion and mamas looked out their best shawls. All wanted to look their best for the highlight of the year.

The only one not looking forward to the event was Seth. He knew without telling what his father thought of him. Seth, the odd one out, who couldn't knock together a hurdle to save his life, much less fashion so intricate an item! Well, he had done his best; the rest was up to Fate.

The last night of the old year was clear and bright, but as the feasting and dancing progressed the clouds blew in.

Bank Vole

BANK VOLES have small eyes and ears and a blunt nose. Mainly found in woodland, they can also live in grassland, hedgerows, bracken and bramble. They make nests under logs, in tree roots or underground.

Adults can be distinguished from the young by the colour of the fur on their backs. Adults have red-brown fur, while younger bank voles have grey-brown fur. Both have creamy-beige fur underneath.

Bank voles feed on fruit, leaves, buds and some insects. They are active during the day and night, but rest in between periods of activity. They have been known to store food in the autumn, preparing for the long winter ahead.

The breeding season begins in March/April and ends in September/October, although an abundant seed crop can sometimes mean that it continues into winter. Four or five young are normally found in each litter and the female bank vole will give birth to five or six litters a year.

Watch out for bank voles if you're planting young trees. They love the bark and have been known to eat young trees completely at ground level. To prevent this happening in your garden, weed vigorously and use plastic tubing to protect the tree.

Wildstock.

Everyone gathered round for the bonfire being lit, and a flare was thrown. Kindling caught, and with a great roar the bonfire burst into life. The tired old globes were flung into the heart of the flames and a loud cheer went up. Fortified by jars of home-brew, the makers of the new globes left the scene to work with frozen fingers at their task. Jemima sent up a fervent prayer for Seth. She had every faith in him, but had he faith in himself?

The bonfire leaped and crackled as one by one the finished globes were presented to the onlookers. Seth was the last to appear. Seeing his handiwork, Jemima dimpled. It more than passed muster; it was his best ever. The Hollybone boys gawped in astonishment, and a smile of approval touched their father's lips.

"Well, then," Seth said to Jemima. "Let's hope my effort lasts the year out."

"Of course it will. It's as good as any here."

"I couldn't have done it without you. In fact," Seth went on, emboldened by the magical glow of success, "I can't be without you."

JEMIMA gazed up at him, the flickering flames throwing shadows across her face. Seth thought he had never seen anything so lovely.

"Jemima, you must know how I feel."

"Tell me," she whispered.

A dozen lines of verse ran through Seth's mind and were rejected. Those had been written in adoration of other maids and this was Jemima, sweet and simple in her retrimmed Sunday gown.

She stood motionless, waiting, and in the end he said the words that had been on his lips for many weeks, words he thought never to utter.

"Jemima, I love you. I can't promise you riches, but whatever else is in my power to give you, you shall have."

"I love you, too," she said in a voice that shook. "Oh, Seth. I've been so fearful. I thought you were growing away from me."

"Then you will be mine?"

"I will. Of course I will!"

His arms enfolded her. The fire burned still, snowflakes spitting. People were leaving for their own firesides, some to hang a new globe to protect hearth and home for the next twelve months, others to sit and ruminate on what a good celebration it had been that time, the best ever. For Seth, it truly was. The light of approval in his father's eye when he had presented his finished globe, bright with berries and glossy leaf, was a memory that would never fade. But best of all, Jemima had given him her promise.

The crowd was thinning now but the couple stayed on, warmed by the glowing embers and the love within them, whilst down in the valley the church bells rang out their New Year message of goodwill and peace to all. ■

If The Hat Fits . . .

WHEN we moved to our cottage in the country dreaming of the Good Life, I'd secretly had this ethereal picture of me in my mind's eye. Wearing a long, floaty Laura Ashley dress, a fetching hat shielding me from the sun's rays, garden trug to hand, I would be found most afternoons drifting around our beautiful garden.

I would lovingly tend the passion flowers and honeysuckle that covered the trellis archway leading to our secluded gazebo, and my roses would be the talk of the county. I could see it all so clearly and I just knew that it was going to work out exactly as I pictured it.

Not that I mentioned any of this to Marcus. He's a practical man rather than a dreamer.

Illustration by Kevin Levell.

by Jennifer Bohnet.

Of course, my rose-tinted dream of how my gardening life in the country would evolve has yet to happen fully in reality, but I have to say that it has been this delightful vision that has kept me going through all the hard physical work.

For over two years there's been more digging than drifting and the garden is still by no means beautiful — but it is slowly coming together. We've been almost self-sufficient in veggies now for eighteen months.

Nothing fancy, just the normal kitchen garden stuff: potatoes, tomatoes, onions, courgettes, garlic, that type of thing. Oh, and honey. Marcus put a bee hive right down at the bottom of the garden near the gnarled apple tree in the bit that I've left to its own devices. It's actually quite pretty, and I love its natural wildness. Marcus calls it my Bellamy plot, after that naturalist who was on TV years ago.

It's the flower garden that is taking time to establish. Gosh, even to call it a flower garden is a bit precious but I'm determined it's going to be one of those old-fashioned English country cottage gardens — a riot of brightly coloured flowers of all shapes and sizes.

I've planted hollyhocks, geraniums, snapdragons, lavender, London pride (that's for my mum, who always had the plant in her garden wherever she was living) and lots of daisies, my favourite flowers.

I've sprayed the roses for greenfly and cut back the honeysuckle. The flower borders are now largely weed free, and there is a second-hand swing seat waiting to be set up on the smooth green lawn at the back. Everything is pointing to the fact that this will finally be the year I drift around the garden and enjoy it.

I've got the long, floaty dress and the trug but I still need a hat to complete the picture. The straw boater I saw today when I went down to the village would be absolutely perfect.

I'M not sure that Marcus was really interested in hearing about the hat I'd seen earlier in the day.

"It's a beautiful old straw boater with a bigger than usual brim. It would shade my face perfectly and with some coloured ribbons tied around the crown it would look so pretty," I told him earnestly as we took the dog for a walk in the fields surrounding our cottage, on a perfect, early summer evening.

The first swallows were swooping above our heads and, from a nearby field, we could hear the sound of a tractor as James, the local farmer, took advantage of the weather to plant another field of cabbages.

"Why didn't you get the hat when you saw it?" Marcus asked. "Anyway, where did you see it? Local charity shop, if I know you. Don't suppose it was that expensive, was it?"

"You're right. I should have got it when I saw it. I've got some books to drop off at the village charity shop tomorrow, so if the hat's still available, I'll definitely get it."

"Good," Marcus said amiably, before changing the subject and telling me about the various attractions he was to be in charge of for the annual village fête.

THE charity shop was busy when I arrived the next morning, but luckily I had the hat corner to myself. I tried a few of the hats on offer just to make absolutely sure I was getting the right one for me. Everything had to be perfect for my dream garden.

The baseball cap was all wrong — it looked quite ridiculous. Then there was a feathery hat that I dithered over for a while before deciding it didn't give enough shade.

The brim of the sombrero was beautifully wide and floppy but the crown was too big for my head. And I looked a real Aunt Sally in the old-fashioned flat porkpie hat. No, the straw boater was definitely the one that had my name on it.

I picked up a packet of mixed ribbons to decorate the crown and paid for my purchases at the till.

"For the garden, is it? That'll keep the sun off nicely," the lady assistant said cheerfully as she took my money and put everything in a large white carrier bag that carried the immortal phrase *Charity Begins At Home*. I beamed at her.

Walking back to the cottage via the track through the fields, I checked there was nobody around. A herd of Jersey cows chewed the cud lazily as they watched me clamber over the gate into the recently ploughed field. Thankfully, there was no sign this morning of James the farmer as I approached Wurzel the scarecrow. Quickly I snatched his hat off and placed my recently purchased sombrero on his large turnip head.

"There you go, Wurzel. You look a proper treat in that," I said. "No self-respecting crow will come anywhere near you." Guiltily I hid the scarecrow's coveted straw boater in the bag and hurried home.

* * * *

This afternoon it was lovely and sunny and I wore my new hat for the first time as I drifted around the garden in my long dress, carrying the trug and a pair of secateurs. The red, yellow and blue ribbons I'd tied around the boater's crown fluttered in the breeze and the brim did a wonderful job of keeping the sun off my face. Even Marcus commented on how pretty my new hat was.

"The charity shop came up trumps there," he declared.

I decided not to tell Marcus where my hat came from. It will remain a secret between Wurzel and me. But I must remember not to wear it to the village fête — just in case anyone recognises it. ■

Sea Fever

by Alice Renaud.

"THIS house is too big for you, Mum."

Ruth's words are still echoing around my head this morning. She's right — my home does feel big today. It floats around me like an old, shapeless cardigan.

For years, this house was so full of life it sometimes looked as though it would burst at the seams. There was me and Gareth, then the children came along, and their pets. Later, Ruth and Owen got married and moved out, but, to my delight, they soon presented me with a brace of grandchildren, who descended on us, joyfully, for every school holiday.

But now it's just me. Ruth and Owen have homes of their own, Ruth in Haverfordwest, Owen in London. Their own children are grown up, and don't want to spend every holiday in an old house in Pembrokeshire. Except Lewis, Ruth's youngest, who loves the sea as much as I do — but even he has less time now that he's started his first job.

We don't need this house any more.

"You won't be able to put off the decision for ever, Winnie," I tell myself.

I run my finger lightly over the kitchen table, feeling the scars and scratches of its wooden surface. This house is my home. I could find my way around it with my eyes closed. Every stone, every object, is packed with memories, especially of Gareth, of all our happy times together. What will I feel when I leave? Won't it be like giving up a part of myself?

The sun dances on the faded tiles, the yellowing walls, the chipped enamel of the cooker. This house doesn't need me, either. It needs — deserves — someone who can look after it properly. Restore it to its former glory.

Soon, I will call Ruth and we'll go and look at some retirement flats.

Soon, but not today. Today, through the window, the sea is winking at me like a big blue eye. Today, I'm going swimming.

Wearing only my bathing suit — well, at this early hour, there's no-one around — I cross the garden, open the gate, and walk down the stone steps that lead to the beach. The sand, washed by the morning tide, is deliciously damp and squishy under my feet. The bright water embraces me.

I've always loved swimming. When I was a child, my favourite story was "The Little Mermaid" by Hans Christian Andersen. Except I could never understand why the Little Mermaid chose to exchange her fishtail for a pair of human legs. If I had had a fishtail, I would never have given it up. I would have spent my entire life in the sea.

I feel I could stay here for hours, floating happily between my two worlds, the blue, warm air above, the green, cool water below. But I'm prudent. I get out before I feel too cold or too tired.

I make my way back to the house, taking care not to slip on the steps or on the garden path. I sing a little wordless tune as I climb the stairs, heading for the bathroom. I'm going to have a shower, wash my hair . . .

Too late, I remember the broken step, halfway up the stairs. I meant to have it fixed; I was waiting for my pension to be paid before organising it.

Too late for that now. I've put my foot squarely in the middle of it, and the wood collapses under my weight with a snap.

So it's true: most accidents do happen in the house, I think, irrelevantly, as the hard, tiled floor rushes up to meet me.

* * * *

"Grandma, are you all right?"

Lewis is peering at me anxiously. I reach across my hospital bed and take his hand.

"I'm fine, love. I fell on my bottom. Good thing I let it expand a bit, eh?"

My grandson laughs, relieved.

"You gave us such a fright!"

"I'm sorry I've caused so much trouble," I mumble.

"Don't be silly, Grandma. We were all really worried about you, that's all."

"As soon as I'm out of hospital," I say firmly, "your mum is going to help me look for a retirement flat. I can't stay in that big house on my own."

"You're right, Grandma." Lewis gazes at me earnestly. "You'll be safer in a flat, with a warden and a manager nearby. You weren't badly hurt and you managed to call an ambulance yourself. Next time you might not be so lucky."

Illustration by David Axtell.

I squeeze his hand.

"I know, Lewis. It's time to let go."

* * * *

The wind sighs around the house, whistling under the eaves and rattling the shutters. I lie in bed, wide awake, listening. I start worrying about the roof — have any of the slates been dislodged? — then I remember that the roof isn't my problem any more. Tonight is my last night in the house. Tomorrow morning, Lewis will drive me to Haverfordwest to begin my new life.

It all happened so quickly. No sooner had the *For Sale* sign appeared outside the house than potential buyers came knocking at the door. Demand is high for large, detached properties by the sea, even those that need a bit of work.

With the proceeds of the sale, I've been able to buy a very nice, roomy two-bedroom flat in a brand-new development, in the centre of Haverfordwest. To my surprise, I even have quite a bit of money left over. A nest egg!

In Haverfordwest, I'll be five minutes away from the shops and buses; Ruth and her husband, David, live just around the corner. I'll catch up with old friends; I know quite a few people in the town. In short, everything is looking rosy. I know I've made the right decision.

So why can't I sleep?

After an hour of tossing and turning, I get up, turn the light on, and wander out of my room on to the landing. The house is cold and smells musty. My favourite pieces of furniture, my books, my pictures, aren't here any more. They're waiting for me in the new flat.

I look around. This was my home. But now, emptied of its objects, its memories, it's just a house. I won't miss it at all. So why do I feel anxious?

I open a window to get rid of the musty smell. The wind rushes in, carrying with it the sound and breath of the sea.

The sea. I can just about make it out if I lean out of the window, into the cold autumn night: a black, moving thing, snuffling at the foot of the garden like a large, friendly animal. I suddenly realise why I feel unsettled. That's what I will miss: not the house itself, but the sea that came with it. My early morning swims. The seagulls, swooping and diving across the sky. Brightly coloured fishing boats, bobbing on the rising tide.

I close the window. I'll get used to living in town. I'm sure I'll still be able to take a trip to the seaside now and again. It's a pity Haverfordwest is not closer to the coast, though. If it had been St Davids, or Pembroke . . .

I smile as I think of Lewis. He works in St Davids, now. So he's close to the sea, but he still misses his sailing.

"Accountancy's all right, Grandma." He sighed over the phone last night. "But I wish I could find a way to spend some time on the sea, rather than just looking at it through a window! Even if it was just in the summer; I could temp in autumn and winter, it's the busy time for accountants anyway."

We're very much alike, he and I.

I go back to bed. And suddenly, as I'm finally about to drift off to sleep, an idea trots into my mind. It will probably look silly in the morning. It's a crazy idea. A wild scheme. I bet Lewis will love it!

* * * *

The gull circles the ship, watching the little boy eat his sandwich. He throws a crust in its direction; the bird swoops down, gobbles the bread, and soars back into the sky effortlessly. The little boy beams. He's having the time of his life.

His father, on the other hand, is looking a little peaky. He's staring at the swaying deck and breathing heavily. I walk up to him.

"Look towards the horizon," I advise him. "Here, have a ginger biscuit."

He nibbles dutifully, and colour slowly returns to his cheeks.

"Your grandmother is amazing," he tells Lewis, who is standing behind us, at the wheel. "I wish I had half her stamina, or her sea legs!"

"Another satisfied customer," Lewis says, as the family wander off to take pictures. "I never thought we'd get bookings so early. Of course, we've been lucky with the weather so far."

I nod happily. I decided not to invest the money from the house sensibly. I bought a boat instead. Lewis looks after it for me, and he's the one who had the idea of starting these "eco-friendly" trips. It began as a hobby, but he's close to turning them into a viable business. He's a very good guide. Visitors to the area enjoy exploring the dramatic coastline, and watching the local wildlife. The best thing is that I can join him on these trips whenever I want.

It wasn't the house I wanted, after all: it was the sea. Now I have the best of both worlds.

"There's one problem, though, Grandma," Lewis says seriously. "We still haven't agreed on a name for the boat. Why won't you let me call it *Winnie*?"

I shake my head.

"I've thought of a better name. Let's call it *The Little Mermaid*."

"Are you sure?" Lewis frowns slightly. "I always thought it's a rather depressing story, isn't it? The poor mermaid gives up her fishtail and her happy life in the sea for the sake of a prince, but he doesn't love her and marries someone else!"

"Ah, but when I was a little girl, I made up an alternative ending. In my version, the mermaid realises her mistake, gets her tail back, and returns to the sea, where she lives happily ever after."

Lewis grins.

"That's all right, then. *The Little Mermaid* it is."

He turns the wheel. The boat leans into the wind like a seagull, and heads west, towards the open sea. ■

Nothing To Declare

by A.J. Redcliffe.

stration by Jim Dewar.

NEVER before in her life had Sheila Campbell committed a crime. Actually, that wasn't quite true. She had been caught speeding once, but that had just been down to a lapse of concentration. She had never deliberately committed an illegal act, a premeditated, planned act. Especially not in a foreign country.

Sheila saw the wing of the aircraft slip down as it lost height to begin its final approach, slicing through thin clouds rushing by, giving an idea of the speed with which things were happening. Her stomach seemed to lurch like the plane.

"Are you OK?"

Sheila looked up into the smiling face of the air stewardess.

"Don't worry," the young woman continued. "Sometimes things get a bit bumpy. It's nothing to be uneasy about."

Sheila managed a weak smile.

"Thank you."

Great heavens, if she looked so frightened now, how would she react if she was questioned? She leaned back and closed her eyes. What could she say if she was caught?

I'm not really a desperate criminal. I'm a respectable, middle-aged Scottish lady, from Edinburgh, actually, a very nice part of Edinburgh. Yes, I realise now it was wrong, but I was under pressure, you see, family pressure.

I did it for my sister, my little sister. Well, she's not so little now, she's married, with children, but I always think of her as my little sister, you see, and when she asked me to do it — she said she was desperate — I said yes, without thinking.

With a slight bump Flight 208 from Glasgow touched down at Logan International Airport, Boston, USA, on January 24, a dull grey afternoon, at 2:17 p.m. local time.

At 2:37 p.m., Sheila was edging forward in the winding queue at Passport Control, a holdall in one hand and clutching in the other the two forms, one green and one white, that she, and all the other passengers, had completed on the plane.

On the green form she had provided her name, date of birth and passport number and had promised faithfully that she was not entering the United States with the intention of overthrowing its government. That was true.

The other form was the white Customs Declaration. She had signed the Declaration — that she had nothing harmful, dangerous or prohibited to declare. That was not true. She had signed it just above the dire printed warning, *All persons are subject to further questioning and their person, belongings, and conveyance are subject to search.*

She shivered at the idea of her "person" being subject to search.

She shuffled on. She would be called forward to the next available high-countered kiosk where Passport Control Officers sat, their dark blue uniforms pressed and pristine, their faces pressed into a uniform expression, not aggressive but certainly not friendly.

Sheila's legs felt shaky. And this wasn't the real test.

Sheila was beckoned forward.
The officer's name tag identified her as Nancy Medina. She flipped through Sheila's passport.

"You came in on the Glasgow flight, Mrs Campbell." She said this without glancing up.

"Yes."

Officer Medina looked up.

"You like living in Glasgow?"

"No!" Sheila replied quickly. "No, I mean I don't live in Glasgow. I live in Edinburgh. I flew from Glasgow, you see."

Officer Medina nodded in agreement. She'd answered correctly.

"Are you here on business?"

"No. On holiday — vacation," she corrected herself into American.

"Where are you staying?"

"Here in Boston. Well, just outside. Cambridge? With my sister. She's married to an American."

"Cambridge is nice," Ms Medina conceded. "OK, Mrs Campbell, have a nice stay." She stamped the passport, clipped part of the green form to it and

Winter In The Cairngorms

BEYOND the world of winter sport,
The chalet and the ski,
There lies a world with danger fraught,
That only few may see.

Here, snowbirds haunt the hoary height,
And alpine flowers glow,
The fox and hare in winter-white
Leave tracks across the snow.

A circling golden eagle casts
Its shadow on the ground,
The snow is deep, the sky is vast,
The silence is profound.

A lonely world of hills and sky,
Both savage and sublime,
Where only nature's laws apply,
Unchanged by passing time.

— Brenda G. Macrow.

Thinkstockphotos.

handed it back.

At 3:12 p.m. Mrs Campbell was admitted to the United States and became subject to its laws and customs, particularly its Customs. Now for the frightening part.

The crowd around the baggage carousel was a jostle three deep with grabbing hands and anxious faces suddenly lighting with joy as an owner identified a suitcase like finding a lost child, and with overloaded trolleys being precariously steered towards Customs, and then freedom.

It was a little while before Sheila managed to get a spot by the clanking carousel as the scrum began to subside. She scanned the moving black belt to try to spot her own case among the various shapes, sizes and colours of luggage tossed carelessly together, the contents of each one private, and for the most part, innocent.

She looked in vain. Several times she thought she saw her case, but each time it was a false alarm. There were fewer and fewer cases. Where was it? Lost? Or found!

Then she saw a policeman standing near to where the carousel snaked through the black plastic flaps. By his side was a dog, a bright-eyed springer spaniel with ears pricked.

She saw the policeman and the dog, just as a tan case with side panels in a Black Watch tartan trundled into view. As the tan and tartan case passed the little white and tan canine, his head cocked to one side and his tail began to sway . . . and Sheila's heart began to palpitate.

The dog moved forward . . . only to be suddenly distracted by a cry of "Sammy!" from two passing airline stewardesses who began to make a fuss of the little dog and the policeman, both of whom seemed equally susceptible to being petted.

In a moment, the case was past the dog and the cop. Mrs Campbell yanked it off the carousel, pulled up the handle and dragged it rapidly away from the dog's dangerous nose.

Because the crowd had thinned to a trickle Sheila had a choice of Customs Officers, or they had their choice of her. Just calm down, she thought. All she had to do was give one of them her white form, smile and walk through pulling her suitcase behind her, just like everyone else was doing. She raised her hand clutching the form and her holdall, ready.

* * * *

"Wait, please! What have you got there?" the Customs Officer said sharply.

Her stomach turned over. Her mouth was dry. Then she realised he had spoken to the man in front of her. He indicated the rucksack slung over the shoulder of the young bearded man and he was pointing particularly to an apple, visible through a webbed pocket of the back-pack, a green apple.

Sheila froze and listened. It transpired that the young man had brought the offending apple with him from his home in Dumbarton. Wasn't he aware that no foreign foodstuffs, plants, flowers, seeds, bulbs, animals, birds or snails, and so forth, could be brought into the United States?

He'd just forgotten about the apple, the young man pleaded.

"Obviously!" the official conceded, but was stony-faced.

"You can eat the apple here, sir, while I watch, or you can hand it over to me, for disposal."

The apple exchanged hands as though it was a hand grenade.

The scene was almost biblical, Sheila thought, and she was next to face the wrath of the almighty one. And it was only a Granny Smith. What would they do to her if they discovered she was carrying an illegal substance?

The young man hurried off in disgrace. The official dropped the offending fruit into a rubbish bin with a thud and turned his attention to Sheila. Should she throw herself on his mercy?

He took her white form, glanced at it, then looked at her.

"Thank you, ma'am. Have a nice stay."

It was 3:59 p.m.

ALISON and her husband, Larry, were waiting for her, and an hour later, Sheila was safely settled in their home in the affluent Boston suburbs. It was dark and cold outside. She could see lights reflected in the icy Charles River in the distance, but her bedroom was warm and brightly lit. She sat on a chair by the window. Her unopened case lay on the bed where Larry had put it.

There was a tap at the door and Alison popped her head round.

"How are you feeling? Tired?"

"Drained," Sheila replied. "Oh, Alison, never again."

"I'm sorry, dear. I shouldn't have asked. I could have got by somehow, I suppose, but . . ." She looked at the suitcase.

"Is it in there?" she asked anxiously.

Sheila stood up, unlocked the case, opened it and removed two layers of clothing and took out a round, heavy object wrapped tightly in a plastic bag.

"It's here," she said.

"Oh, thank you," Alison said eagerly, her hands reaching out and beginning to unwrap it.

"I've promised Larry and some of our friends a real occasion tomorrow night and a taste of the real thing. You just can't get it here. The Americans are so sniffy about things like this."

She finished the unwrapping.

"Oh, Sheila, it's perfect. You can't have a good Burns Night supper without a real haggis, can you? A genuine taste of Scotland. And you shall have the honour of carving it, dear." ■

Badger

ONE of Britain's favourite mammals, badgers are nocturnal and elusive. Very social creatures, they live together in underground setts which are a series of tunnels with separate nest chambers, toilets and several entrances.

Badgers inherit these setts from their parents and go on to expand and refine them. The resulting tunnel systems can be centuries old.

A male badger is called a boar, a female is a sow and a young badger is a cub. There are eight species of badger and the one most common in the UK today is the Melinae. Badgers are omnivores and mainly eat earthworms, insects and grubs. They also eat fruit, birds, reptiles, amphibians and small mammals. Badgers catch most of their food by digging and have been known to do so with amazing speed.

Badgers are very popular in English fiction and you might remember characters such as Tommy Brock in Beatrix Potter's "The Tale Of Mr Tod" or Badger from "The Wind In The Willows" by Kenneth Grahame. J.K. Rowling more recently used the badger as the official mascot for Hufflepuff, one of the houses at Hogwarts school, in her famous Harry Potter stories.

Wildstock.

My Funny Valentine

by Sheila Norton.

NOBODY took any notice of Valentine's Day in our house. The boys were too young, the dog was too old, and I — I was too busy. That was my excuse, anyway. Better than admitting the truth — that the most romantic thing that ever came through my letter-box was the gas bill.

So last February fourteenth, when a huge pink envelope dropped on the mat, I just thought junk mail was being delivered in strange packaging these days. When I opened it, I gave such a gasp that the dog shot under the table and the children ran downstairs in excitement.

"What is it?" Benjamin yelled.

"It's not your birthday!" Adam said, looking at the card suspiciously. "Oh! It's a Valentine!"

"Who's it from?" they both demanded, looking amazed, as well they might.

"No idea. I'll put it back in the envelope for now," I said — too late. The twins had got hold of it and were killing themselves laughing.

"*To the One I Love*," Benjamin read out loud. "*From Your Secret Admirer.*"

"You sure it's for you, Mum?" Adam said. "There's nothing on the envelope."

"The Secret Admirer must have put it through the door himself." Benjamin sniggered. "*To the One I Love*! Yuck!"

"People of my age do have admirers, you know," I said, a bit crossly. I was only forty-two. In a good light I could still pass for — well, forty-two, probably. "We don't just sink into middle-age and slippers when we turn forty, you know."

I checked my feet. Slippers. I ignored the boys' giggling and shooed them back upstairs to get ready for school.

* * * *

"It can't be for me," I told my friend, Nicola, at work. "I hardly even know any men these days."

"Your ex-husband?"

"Of course not! Rob never sent me anything like that even when we were first married! I don't think he knows when Valentine's Day is."

"Well, perhaps it's someone from here. What about Simon in Accounts?"

"If only!" I smiled. Simon was gorgeous — tall, slim, blond — and at least ten years younger than me, with a steady girlfriend. I felt my smile fading.

"Well, anything's possible," Nicola said. "That's what's fun about this kind of thing. The card could be from anyone! Who would you like it to be from?"

* * * *

"Why do you keep grinning to yourself?" Adam asked later, as I was cooking dinner.

"Oh — just thinking," I said vaguely.

"Did you find out who your Valentine was from?" Benjamin giggled.

"No, but I'm thinking it could be George Clooney."

"Who?" Adam said.

"Probably some film star from the old days," Benjamin told him sagely.

I was in the middle of burning the sausages when a fabulous red sports car pulled up outside. I watched from the

Illustration by Pat Gregory.

kitchen window as the driver got out of the car and walked slowly up the path, and then stood, looking at my front door. I held my breath. Whoever he was, he could actually pass for George Clooney at a distance.

"Who's that?" Benjamin demanded loudly behind me, making me jump so that I dropped the frying-pan and the burnt sausages rolled across the floor.

"I don't know. One of your teachers?" I suggested. "You're not in trouble, are you?"

"No!" he squawked indignantly.

Well, whoever he was, he was now knocking at the door.

"Go and play!" I told the children, hustling them quickly into the other room.

I opened the door and Red Car Man gave a cough, looking very ill-at-ease.

"Hello. Sorry to disturb you, but I wondered if you got any . . . unexpected post this morning?"

"Ah." I should have guessed! "Yes. I'll go and get it. Actually, why don't you come in for a moment? It's freezing out there."

HE followed me into the kitchen and stood waiting awkwardly while I rummaged through the free newspapers and junk mail on the table.

"Here it is." I turned to him with the card. Under my kitchen lights, he looked even nicer. But he was staring at the pink envelope nervously.

"Is that mine?"

"Well, I presume so . . ." I was confused now. I mean, how many men were likely to knock on my door tonight wanting Valentine's cards back? "Don't you recognise it?"

Tentatively, he pulled the card out of the envelope, holding it by the edges as if it might bite. When he saw the massive red heart on the front, and the pink fluffy bunnies holding red roses, he almost dropped it.

"*To the One I Love*," he read. He looked back at me, alarmed. "This has nothing to do with me!"

"Oh!" was all I could think to say. "I'm so sorry!"

"You thought I sent you this?"

"No, no, of course not!"

"I mean, not that I wouldn't — I'm sure if I knew you . . ."

"Of course you wouldn't!" I broke off, and started to laugh sheepishly. "I knew it wasn't meant for me. So I just presumed, when you called . . ."

"I don't know which of us is the more embarrassed!" He laughed, too. "What I actually came for was a letter."

"What kind of letter?" I looked around the kitchen, like I might find one under a saucepan.

"Probably a brown envelope. Probably postmarked from the hospital."

"Oh. No, sorry — nothing like that's turned up here. Should it have done?"

"I'm waiting for some results. They should have come by now. Turns out the hospital had my address wrong. I live at 46, Coniston Drive . . ."

Blackrock Cottage, Glencoe

A **FAMILIAR** sight as part of the West Highland Way, Blackrock Cottage is one of the most photographed buildings in Scotland. Many remember it as their first view of the Buachaille Etive Mor and Glencoe — a glen with a multitude of views that keep folk coming back time and again!

Thinkstockphotos.

"And they sent the letter to Coniston Road? Well, it hasn't arrived." I watched his face. "Couldn't they tell you your results over the phone?"

"No. They were just forwarding them on for me. Well, I'll have to get a copy sent. I'm sorry for troubling you, um . . .?"

"Emma."

"I'm Joseph. Joseph Palmer."

Ridiculously, we shook hands, and then started laughing again.

As he left, he added, grinning, "I would have sent the card. If I'd known you."

"Has the Red Car man gone?" Benjamin said disappointedly, bursting back into the kitchen. "I was hoping he was your Secret Valentine!"

"'Course he wasn't!" Adam laughed before I had a chance to answer. "He looked young. Well, younger than Mum."

"Never mind." Benjamin tried to console me. "Perhaps he didn't want to stay for dinner because he saw you drop the sausages."

NICOLA was impressed, though.

"Tell me again what he looked like! Tell me again what he said about the Valentine card!"

"Actually, Nic, I'm more concerned about his test results. He might be suffering from something awful."

"Did he look sick?"

"No," I admitted. "He looked gorgeous! But it could be . . . something nasty that doesn't show."

I'd almost forgotten about my mystery Valentine's card — I was far too anxious about the health of Joseph Palmer!

The letter was on the doormat when I got home.

Mr J Palmer

46, Coniston Road.

Honestly. Wouldn't you have thought a hospital would be more careful about their patients' addresses? If Joseph hadn't called round the previous night, I wouldn't have had any idea who he was. He might be waiting to find out

Saint Valentine's Day

THIS is the day that the garden birds
Begin to build a nest.
This is the day of St Valentine —
A day that's truly blessed.
This is the day that sweethearts
Swear that their love is true.
This is the day that cards arrive —
From whom? We wish we knew!
This is the day of promises,
And all the joys they bring,
For this is the day that winter
Looks forward to coming spring.

— Dorothy Morris.

whether he needed an operation, or it could be really bad news. Would they put that sort of thing in a letter?

I had to take the boys to football practice later, and returned home via Coniston Drive. By the time I'd reached No. 46 I'd worked myself up into a frenzy of concern.

"It came today," I announced, handing him the letter as soon as he opened the door. "I do hope it isn't bad news."

"Oh! Thanks." He smiled. It didn't look like the smile of someone with a dreadful illness. "It was good of you to bring it round." He hesitated, and then went on. "I know it's a cheek, Emma — but would you mind staying with me while I open it? I'm so nervous about the result, I'll probably just sit and stare at the envelope all evening otherwise."

"Oh — sure, of course." I followed him into the house. It was like mine, but without the clutter. In fact, it didn't look lived-in at all.

"I live on my own," he said, looking around the lounge as if he was seeing it for the first time. "And I haven't been here much. I've been spending a lot of time at the hospital."

"Sorry to hear that."

"I know. Not a lot of fun. Well — here goes." He closed his eyes for a moment and then ripped open the envelope. I could actually hear the clock ticking as he studied the single sheet of paper inside.

"YES!" he shouted suddenly — and before I knew it, I'd been lifted off my feet and engulfed in a hug. "Oh, I'm so sorry!" he exclaimed as he put me back down again, but he couldn't keep the grin off his face. "I got a bit carried away."

"That's OK." It had taken me by surprise, but I didn't feel I could deny a sick man a little hug — or, hopefully, a man who wasn't sick after all? "Good news?" I asked.

"The best!" He laughed happily. "Look, Emma, you haven't got to rush off, have you?"

"Well, no . . . the twins are at football practice till half-past seven."

"Would you have a quick glass of something with me? To celebrate?" He looked at me steadily. "Unless your husband is expecting you back?"

"No husband any more. He found someone else, seven years ago."

"That's awful," he muttered. "Red or white?"

"She was blonde, but . . ."

"Wine!" He turned to me, a bottle in each hand, and we both laughed. "Which?"

"Either. Thanks." I watched him fill two glasses.

"Well, here's to you," I said. "Glad it's good news. I presume — you've got the all-clear?"

I felt awkward about asking. He was giving me a very strange look.

"All-clear? Well, that's one way of putting it. I passed, thank goodness." He took a gulp of his wine, realised I was looking puzzled, and added, "My FRCS exam. It means I can apply for a consultant's post, and finally stop working these killer junior doctor's hours."

"You're a doctor?" I said faintly.

"Yes! Sorry, didn't I say?"

"The letter didn't say Doctor Palmer."

"I'm a surgeon. Surgeons are misters. Strange British quirk, something to do with surgeons originally being barbers, apparently — oh, my word. You thought the letter was about those sort of test results!"

"I was afraid you had some dreadful illness." I tried to hide my embarrassment behind my wine glass. "I'm so glad you're OK."

He smiled at me — a lovely, gentle smile — and I decided that close up, he didn't actually look like George Clooney at all. Even nicer.

"I'm fine, thank you, Emma," he said, looking straight into my eyes. "In fact, do you know what? I've never felt better."

* * * *

"Ooh!" Nicola gazed at me with her mouth and eyes wide open. "And then did he kiss you?"

"Mind your own business!" I replied primly, trying to keep the grin off my face. "But I'm seeing him again tomorrow night."

"I'm really pleased for you," she said softly. "Oh, well, the Valentine kind of worked, then, in a roundabout way, didn't it?"

"But I still don't know who . . ." I stared at her, suddenly suspicious.

"It was me," she admitted. "Well, every Valentine's Day you complain about not getting any cards. Yes, you do!" she insisted, before I'd had a chance to argue. "I thought a little mystery might cheer you up."

"Thanks for nothing!" But I laughed. "I might just keep your card as a souvenir. I rather like the big red heart on the front."

"In love already, are you?" she teased.

"No," I said, laughing. "But I am going out with a heart surgeon!" ■

A Gift From Mrs Parker

by Teresa Ashby.

Illustration by David Axtell.

WE both stared at the letter in the middle of the table. It looked out of place among the debris of breakfast, like a peacock among plump brown hens.

"I think you should open it," my brother Michael said. "It looks important."

"But why would a solicitor be writing to me?" I said. "I haven't done anything wrong."

"Are you sure about that?" He wiggled his eyebrows at me and I glared at him.

"Of course I'm sure."

"It doesn't have to be bad news," Michael said. "Open it."

So with trembling hands I did, and as I read the contents I went from relief to disbelief to amazement.

Even Michael began to look worried.

"What is it?"

"Mrs Parker, Gran's old neighbour, has left me something in her will."

"Phew. That's nice of her," Michael said.

"She's left me her dog."

Mrs Parker was a lovely lady. She'd been a good friend to Gran and we'd kept in touch with her after Gran moved to the Isle of Wight to live with my aunt.

She had a huge network of friends and sometimes she would come to spend Christmas with us. Occasionally she'd go down to the island for a few days to stay with my aunt and gran.

My chin started to wobble.

I was thrilled that she'd left me her dog, but I didn't think Mum would be very happy. I'd always wanted a dog, but Mum wasn't keen so I'd spent my childhood taking other people's dogs out for walks.

CASEY was a three-year-old Jack Russell who thought he was an Irish Wolfhound. Mum tolerated him when Mrs Parker came to stay last summer for my sister's wedding, but she wasn't happy.

I thought he was lovely, though. He'd jump on to my lap and curl up like a cat and at mealtimes he'd sit and grin at me until I slipped him a treat.

"He's staying with her next-door neighbour at the moment."

Mum came in then with her arms full of laundry. She stuffed it all in the machine then started to clear away the breakfast things.

"What's up?" she said. "You look upset."

"Not exactly upset," I said and I showed her the letter.

"I'm sure someone else will take him in," Mum said when I told her the news. "It wouldn't be practical for us to have a dog here."

"But I'd take him for walks and I'd look after him," I said, and suddenly I felt thirteen instead of twenty-three.

And apart from the fact that I desperately wanted to give Casey a home, Mrs Parker had trusted me to do just that. I couldn't let her down.

The following day, two more letters arrived from the solicitor. Michael

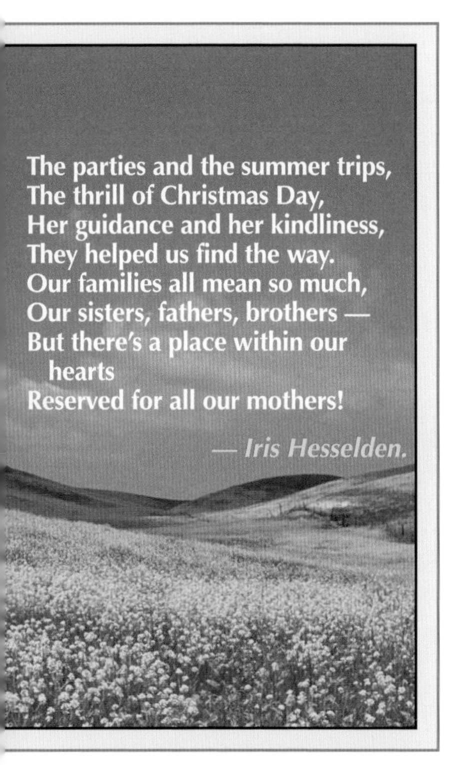

opened his and his face lit up.

"Mrs Parker has left me her car."

"That old thing!" Dad laughed. "It's neither use nor ornament, but you might get something for scrap value."

Michael went pale at the thought. Mrs Parker hadn't driven her old car for years, but Michael used to go into her garage to visit it when we went to see her. He loved the smell of the old vehicle and said it had proper class and character.

"I can get it going again," he said. He'd often offered to have a look at it for Mrs Parker, but she used to say her driving days were over.

"We can't have it here," Mum said with the same finality of tone she'd used over the dog.

When she opened her letter, she sat down and put her hand over her mouth.

"I don't believe it," she whispered. "Mrs Parker has left us her caravan in Southwold. I didn't even know she had a caravan in Southwold."

"Great," Dad said. "We can go there for weekends."

"We certainly cannot," Mum huffed. "How can we go away? I have so much to do here. We have so many ties."

"What ties?" Dad said, looking baffled. "Our children are all grown up. Most of them have left home."

Mum waved her hand about.

"Grown up they might be, but they still need us. And what about our grandchildren?"

"I'm off to work," Dad said, shaking his head.

As I walked to work, I thought of dear little Casey with his bright brown eyes and eager expression. If I didn't have him, where would he go? Would Mrs Parker's neighbour keep him?

Mrs Parker knew very well that Mum didn't like dogs, and there must have been dozens of other people she could have left him to. So why me? I thought back to the last time I'd seen her. It was last summer, when she'd come for the wedding.

"Not courting yet, Zara?" she'd asked with a mischievous gleam in her eye.

"Not at the moment," I said.

"Good for you. How old are you? Twenty-two? Plenty of time yet. You don't want to get stuck in a rut at your age — or are you already?"

I thought her choice of words was strange at the time. How could I be stuck in a rut? I was young, free and single. But as I walked along I realised she was right.

I was still living at home, having my meals cooked for me by Mum. I was in a rut already — a cosy one, granted, but a rut all the same.

And what about Mum? She'd said she couldn't use the caravan because of her family ties. That wasn't right, surely. My parents deserved better than that.

About halfway between home and work, I passed a row of Victorian terraced houses that looked over the park. Several were either for sale or rent and I'd often thought how nice it would be to live there.

It was almost as if Mrs Parker had left me a shovel with which to dig myself out.

As soon as I got to work, I called the estate agent and arranged to view a couple of the flats. Both were basements with full use of the garden. A garden would be essential if Casey was going to live with me.

And being opposite the park couldn't be better. I could take him for walks before and after work and it was close enough for me to nip home in my lunch-hour to spend some time with him instead of eating lunch at my desk as I normally did. It would also be nice and handy for visiting Mum and Dad.

I couldn't believe it at lunchtime when I went to view one of the flats and bumped into my brother.

"What are you doing here?" I said.

"Just looking," he said, grinning. "This flat comes with a garage in a block down the road. I could keep Mrs Parker's car in there while I'm doing it up."

"You're really serious about that old car?"

"Yes, I am," he said. "I know I can get it going. Anyway, I'm twenty-eight now, it's time I got a place of my own."

"Oh, dear," I said. "I wonder how Mum is going to feel about that."

"You tell her your news first," he said. "And we'll see how she takes it, then I'll break it to her that I'm leaving home, too."

When I got home from work, Mum was sitting at the kitchen table with the solicitor's letter in her hand.

She looked up and rubbed her hand across her eyes.

"Mrs Parker was a lovely lady," she said. "I'll miss her visits."

"So will I," I said.

"I didn't realise how late it had got," she said, hurrying to get up. "I'd better get dinner on."

This was how it always was. Mum rushing about getting meals for us, doing the washing and ironing.

"I think you should use the caravan," I said as I set the table.

"Don't be silly, dear," she said. "I have far too much to do."

"You wouldn't have if Michael and I left home," I said.

She froze in the middle of chopping potatoes.

I thought she was going to explode, but she turned to look at me.

"Well, I wouldn't want you to leave home just so I could go to Southwold now and then," she said.

"But it might be better if I left home if I'm going to have a dog."

"You're serious about having Casey, then?" She sighed. "I'm not surprised. He seemed very taken with you, and you with him."

She smiled, threw the potato back into the saucepan and hugged me.

"When Mrs Parker was here last summer she said I should get away more. Sea air, she said, would put roses in my cheeks. I thought she meant I should go and visit Gran on the island."

"I think Mrs Parker knew exactly what she was talking about," I said. "You and Dad have spent most of your lives looking after us. It's time you had some time to yourselves and time Michael and I got out of our cosy rut and set out on our own."

The decisions had been made. It was time to move on.

I LOVE my little flat. It's not very big, but it's cosy and perfect for Casey and me. The fact that my brother lives ten doors down is nice, too. We're still close, but without being in each other's pockets.

My life has changed in so many ways. Mum helped me make the curtains for the flat and she often comes to visit. The funny thing is, she'll sit in the chair by the window overlooking my little garden and Casey will hop on to her lap and curl up like a cat.

And she doesn't mind a bit. She's already been to Mrs Parker's caravan three times and has fallen in love with Southwold — and I think she's fallen in love with Dad all over again.

I've noticed that when they walk round here to visit me, they often hold hands, and they're talking about selling the house and getting a bungalow on the other side of the park.

The odd thing is that since Michael and I left home, our family has felt more like a family. My cousins come round to visit and sometimes they stay over.

Moving out has brought us closer together. Doesn't that sound daft?

And you'd be amazed how many people I've met since I've been walking Casey in the park every day. There's one in particular. He's called Anthony and he has a pair of scatty spaniels.

And my brother has started seeing the girl who lives in the flat above his. I think Mrs Parker would approve. I think she knew exactly what she was doing all along. ■

A Break With Tradition

AS I lay the table early on this special Sunday morning, Jess, my Border collie, sticks tirelessly to my heels, as though she knows how hard this is for me. The house is completely silent. We're alone, just as I'd wanted.

There, almost done. I place a vase of yellow daffodils in the centre of the table, tuck folded white linen napkins into the glasses and straighten the cutlery at each place setting.

It's not something to be rushed. I pad in slippered feet around the stone kitchen floor and there's not a sound except the soft tap-tap of Jess's faithful feet behind me.

I never thought I'd do this again. There's a tear in my eye as I stand back to admire my handiwork: the huge oak table, a family heirloom, looks a picture. It was made for occasions like this. It'll seat ten comfortably, although it's been over two years since more than just a few of us sat down for a meal. But today is going to be different.

As I place the final, special chair at the head of the table, I can't help but smile and remember how it all began, two springs ago. The first spring without my darling Dougie . . .

* * * *

"Sorry, Nan, must dash — I'm on my lunch break!" My granddaughter was at my door, looking pencil-slim in her work suit and pressing a bunch of flowers into my arms, a thank you for her recent birthday present.

It was a cold, bright day, just like

the day she'd been born, twenty-five years earlier, when the apple trees in our little orchard were in full bloom, like five white brides. My husband, Dougie, had suggested Blossom for the baby's name but our son had laughed it off, saying it sounded too much like one of our milking herd and, of course, he was right.

They called the baby Esther and she was the apple of my Dougie's eye for the rest of his life.

by Helen Yendall.

Illustration by Mandy Murray.

"Oh, Esther, love, can't you even manage a quick cup of tea?" I scolded her then. She looked pale and drawn. She was always rushing these days.

She glanced at her watch. Everything was always perfectly timetabled with Esther.

"I'm on my way into town, to choose the favours for the wedding."

I shook my head but stayed quiet. It wasn't my wedding, after all, and she was so excited. Her marriage to Eddie was still a few months off but there seemed a never-ending list of things to arrange and, Esther being Esther, it all had to be perfect: videos, photographers, menus and cars and now favours for the guests. It was so different from how things were in my day.

Esther looked thoughtful for a second.

"I will come in, then, just for a few minutes," she said and stepped through into the kitchen.

When she saw the dozens of photos spread out across the table, her hands flew to her face.

"Oh, look, photos of me — and me and Papa! Loads of them!"

She'd found the pile of pictures I'd set aside of Esther as a baby — most of them with her beloved grandfather, my Dougie.

She turned to me, her eyes swimming.

"Oh, Nan, I feel awful! Here I am dashing around, thinking of myself as usual and you're here on your own, poring over photos and reminiscing . . . "

I shushed her with a chuckle.

"You daft thing, that's not what I'm doing at all. It's something for your wedding but it was supposed to be a secret!" I quickly tucked the cardboard frame under the table. "I forgot I'd left them out the instant I saw your car draw up!"

The montage of baby pictures of Esther and her fiancé — a joint enterprise with Eddie's mother to amuse the wedding guests — would have to wait.

"Now just pretend you haven't seen me doing all this, won't you? It can be our little secret," I said, filling the kettle and placing it on the Aga.

Esther laughed and agreed, so as we chatted over our tea we left the photos out, both of us glancing fondly at Dougie's familiar smiling face looking up at us.

"How are all the wedding plans going?" I asked.

She sighed heavily and ran her hands through her hair.

"There's still so much to do! I've got a list as long as my arm — you wouldn't believe it. The invitations still haven't arrived, the bridesmaid dresses are a disaster and —"

I laid my hand gently on hers.

"Esther, a wedding is supposed to be a happy occasion. It doesn't have to be perfect. This isn't the movies, you know."

She shrugged her shoulders.

"Well, what was it like when you married Papa?"

"There was still rationing after the war, so I almost didn't have a wedding dress, for starters." I smiled. "All the family had to rally round and collect food points so we could have enough ingredients for a cake. Just one tier, mind!"

"Weren't you stressed, Nana? I'd have been tearing my hair out!"

I smiled.

"I don't think stress had been invented then. All that mattered was that I was marrying the man I loved and that I was going to spend the rest of my life with him."

"That's how I feel about Eddie," Esther said. She glanced at the photos covering the table. "Doesn't it make you sad, though, Nana, looking at these pictures, with all their memories?"

I shook my head and smiled.

"I had almost fifty perfect years with him. How many people can say that? And as for the memories? No, they don't make me sad: the memories are what keep me going."

Esther picked up one of the photos of her and Dougie. When she was a little girl she had almost lived with me in the farmhouse, while her parents, her uncles and Dougie were out with the animals or tending the crops on the farm.

Hedgehog

DID you know that hedgehogs got their name because of their pig-like habit of rooting noisily through the undergrowth for food? Easily recognisable because of their spines, hedgehogs tend to be nocturnal and mainly eat insects.

A very powerful form of natural pest control, a single hedgehog can eat up to 200 grams of insects every night. If you'd like to attract a hedgehog into your garden, try leaving out small amounts of tinned cat or dog food. Make sure, however, that you use the chicken varieties and not the fish as they do not like the taste. Water in a container with very low sides is also welcome as hedgehogs can become very thirsty.

One point to bear in mind, however, is that hedgehogs can become very ill if they eat too many insects which have ingested chemical insecticides. This poisons the hedgehog and can result in death.

Hedgehogs are very vocal and communicate with each other in grunts, snuffles, squeaks or squeals. They can live for a relatively long time — larger species of hedgehogs have been known to survive four to seven years in the wild.

Baby hedgehogs are born with a protective membrane covering their quills, which are just below the skin. Once the membrane has been cleaned off, the quills pass through the skin and the hedgehog has its own natural defence system.

Wildstock.

In the picture, she was about three years old, riding a Shetland pony, and Dougie was holding the reins. They had identical grins.

"I miss Papa so much," she said, a little break in her voice. "I wish he could be at my wedding."

I patted her hand.

"Oh, I think he will be. I really think he will. Do you know, I've just had an idea about those favours of yours. How many do you think you're going to need?"

And so it was agreed. When Esther got married that September, there were no almonds wrapped in tissue, or chocolates or tiny perfume favours on their wedding breakfast table. Instead, each guest had a little green apple from my Dougie's orchard by the side of their plate to remind them, as my son said so tenderly in his father-of-the-bride speech, that Esther had been the apple of her grandfather's eye.

SUDDENLY Jess lets out a bark and I move to the window and look out across the pasture. She's heard a car way down on the drive and her tail wags in anticipation. Any minute now, Esther and my three daughters-in-law will be arriving, to help me prepare the Sunday roast — our first family meal for a long time.

The men will be along a little later, when they've done their chores. Even on this Mothering Sunday, we women will be doing the cooking, but that's the way it's always been and I certainly don't mind.

As Dougie always used to say, there's no rest for the wicked when you work on a farm.

The side of beef is already in the oven and the delicious waft of cooking meat is starting to seep through the kitchen, bringing with it memories of many other happy family occasions just like this one.

I'm enjoying my last few moments of solitude, remembering those lovely times of the past, when Dougie would sit at one end of the table and I'd sit at the other, opposite him, watching as he expertly carved the tender meat. When everyone's plate was filled, he'd stay standing, raise his glass in a toast, smiling at the happy faces around him, always saving the best smile, and a wink, for me.

I never thought I could do this again. I couldn't bear to see that empty seat at the head of the table, or to fill it with anyone else.

But that's all changed since Jamie Douglas Stevenson was born, my Esther's darling boy. It's her first Mother's Day and I wanted to make it a memorable one — and the special seat at the head of the table is Jamie's highchair.

That's his place now and I smile as I imagine him sitting there, later, gurgling happily, and I'm sure of one thing — my Dougie would have most certainly approved. ■

A Match Made In Heaven

"YOU'D best nip out for a breath of fresh air, Bessie. It's a trifle warm in here."

Warm? It was like a furnace in that kitchen, what with Cook baking bread, stewing mutton and boiling jam.

"Thank you, Mrs Bray. I do declare it's making me come over all funny." I pushed damp curls back from my brow.

She pursed her lips as if she thought all kitchen-maids poor, weak creatures.

"Just sweep up that pile of mud under the table before you go, girl."

What a mess I found! There were great chunks of dirt, clay and all.

"It's that new gardener who started yesterday." Mrs Bray folded her arms disapprovingly. "Came in here for his breakfast with his boots on, the great dozy creature."

I laughed.

"So what's he like? Old, wizened and grumpy like the last one?"

"No, he's a giant of a man with huge feet and plenty of lip, too. He wasn't the least bit ashamed when I told him off. 'Nothing wrong with a bit of good, honest earth, Ma,' he said. The cheek of it!"

by Mary Kettlewell.

Illustration by Len Thurston.

I was hard put not to smile at the affronted look on Mrs Bray's face. I swept up the mud without further delay and headed for the vegetable patch, hoping I might catch a sight of the gardening giant. It wasn't often we had the excitement of a new member of staff at Lord Hareham's.

"Bring some cabbage back with you, Bessie," Mrs Bray called through the window. "And I don't want any with slugs in!"

It was a relief to get out into the cool, clear air. As I hurried along the path I saw the new gardener, looking for all the world like Goliath, that giant man the parson had told us all about the previous Sunday. Six foot four he must have been, with size twelve boots and shoulders the breadth of a barn door. He was banging away with a hammer at lengths of metal rod laid out on his Lordship's lawn.

I **WATCHED** him out of the corner of my eye as I bent down to pull up the cabbages. But I didn't see the flowerpot lurking under a leek, and it broke beneath my foot with a sharp crack.

"Shirking the potato-peeling, eh, maid?" he called cheerfully.

I flushed scarlet.

"I thought gardeners planted and weeded things," I said shyly. "What are you doing with all that scrap iron?"

"Master's orders." He winked. "He needed a skilled job done, so he asked Luke Strangeways."

He looked me up and down, and I wished that my apron wasn't so dirty and smudged, for no girl wants a fellow to see her all dowdy and dull. But he didn't seem to notice.

"What may your name be, maid?" he asked boldly.

"Bessie," I replied. "I'm first kitchen-maid."

He took a wooden ball from the box that lay beside him and tossed it into the air, catching it neatly.

"You know what this is, Bessie?"

"It's a wooden ball," I said, puzzled.

"And this?" He held up a curious-shaped hoop.

"For growing peas?" I guessed.

"Nothing to do with vegetables." He grinned. "This is a croquet hoop. It's a game they play in France, from what I'm told, and the master's fallen for it good and proper."

"And what are those?" I pointed to several strange-looking wooden objects with long handles and ends shaped like gun barrels.

Before he could tell me, Mrs Bray's voice rang out loud and clear from the kitchen window.

"I said to get a breath of fresh air and pick a few cabbages, Bessie, not spend the day gossiping to all and sundry. There's work to be done!"

Luke waved cheekily in the direction of the kitchen window.

"You've got a right tartar there! How about taking a stroll by the river with me after you've finished work? I'll tell you all about these mallets."

I could see what Mrs Bray had meant about cheek, for he had known me for all of five minutes and was already thinking of moonlit walks by the river. I felt quite bashful; I was only nineteen, and unused to the company of men. But I must confess a little shiver ran down my spine. A girl could feel safe, surely, with such a strong man by her side.

"Maybe, maybe not," I hedged. "The way things are going I'll be up to my eyes in the scullery till long past dark." I was pleasantly surprised and flattered to see a look of disappointment flit over his face.

I **MENTIONED** it to Mrs Bray as we washed up after dinner, and she turned all motherly, as was her way sometimes.

"Take an old woman's advice, girl. Don't stand for any nonsense where men are concerned. Give as good as you get, and don't be taken in by their wiles." For all her sharpness, she was a kindly soul.

As it was we finished quite early, and Mrs Bray, worn out by all her baking and cooking, decided to have a lie-down. I went outside to find the master's lawn transformed, with hoops set up all over it and two striped posts at either end. Luke, mallet in hand, was aiming a ball through one of the hoops.

"You're just in time, Bessie," he said when he spotted me. "Some of the hoops are on the narrow side. We'll take them back to the workshop and open them out a bit more."

I recalled Mrs Bray's words.

"*We*, Luke?" I said archly. "What makes you think I'm going to turn blacksmith's assistant all of a sudden?"

He laughed.

"My apologies. I should have realised you wouldn't want to sully those lily-white hands of yours."

I had to smile, despite blushing red as the master's hunting jacket.

Off we went to the shed, where Luke secured a hoop in the vice.

"Now you sit yourself down on that bale, Bessie, while I work on this. I was only teasing before — it's no job for a maid."

His tone was kind, and I realised Mrs Bray had been wrong. There was more to Luke than just brawn and muscle.

Soon we were chatting away like old friends.

"Where do you hail from, Bessie?" he asked.

"Over Lowestoft way. My folks run a kipper-smoking house."

"So you left home and chose the life of a kitchen-maid?" Before I could reply he leaned closer and inhaled deeply. "Your hair smells like roses on a summer's day. Not a hint of kipper smoke!"

"Be done with you. I've never heard such nonsense!" But his words touched my heart. No-one had ever paid me such a compliment before.

"And how about you, Luke? What's your story?"

"I've no family, save a brother somewhere on the high seas. Lord Hareham's manager was looking for a handyman at the hiring fair, and seemed to think I'd fit the bill." He chuckled. "Told me he'd meant to buy a horse, but I was cheaper and looked stronger!"

I glanced admiringly at him.

"And the croquet?"

"They say a posh Irish lady saw French farm workers playing it with broomsticks and hoops made of willow rods. She brought the idea home, and it spread like wildfire."

Footsteps crunched on the gravel and I looked up to see Lord Hareham himself approaching.

"How's it going, Strangeways?"

"Fine, sir. The hoops were a bit narrow, so I've been widening them with the help of Bessie here."

If I wasn't mistaken, I saw the beginnings of a twinkle in his Lordship's eye.

"Is that so? Well, I can lend a hand now."

Luke was a quick thinker, that was clear.

"Begging your pardon, sir, but the damp grass will spoil your boots. Bessie can hold the hoops while I tap them in."

Lord Hareham was a kindly soul, and he could see Luke fancied my company for the task.

"That sounds like a good idea, Strangeways. Just make sure everything is ready for the croquet party on Saturday."

ONCE his Lordship had gone, Luke and I started pacing out the hoops and tapping them home.

"We'd best check everything is in order," Luke said presently. "You take the first shot, Bessie. I'll show you how."

He stood behind me, and closed his hands over mine as I took a swing. Clunk! The ball wobbled across the grass and missed the hoop by a good two feet — and no wonder, for my heart was thudding.

By the time I reached the fifth hoop, however, my eye was in and the ball shot through the hoop clean as a whistle.

"My, you're a grand player, Bessie."

I felt a warm glow at his generous words of praise.

* * * *

By Friday afternoon the croquet pitch was in perfect condition. Mrs Bray and I had been hard at work all day, preparing food for the party, so by the time my head hit my pillow I was ready for a good night's sleep.

It wasn't to be. Whether it was an owl in the oak tree or the bright moon shining in through my window, I couldn't say, but I woke with a start and jumped out of bed.

The sight that met my eyes was one of devastation. The croquet lawn was covered in mounds of earth thrown up by the moles. A croquet tournament in

Blackpool

WITH so-called "staycations" the new in thing, resorts like Blackpool are experiencing an upturn in business. And quite rightly — this wee seaside town has been a favourite for many years, with something for everyone, from a dip in the sea to a dance in the ballroom, fairground rides and proper fish and chips!

the morning? There was no chance!

I dressed hurriedly and ran over to the gardener's cottage.

"Luke!" I banged my fist on the door. "Wake up!"

He appeared just a few minutes later, clad in his old gardening clothes, and stared at the lawn in disbelief.

"All that work, and now look at it. There's nowt we can do, Bessie."

I wasn't going to be defeated by a few moles.

"Yes, there is. We'll have to shovel off the earth and level the surface."

"But it's the middle of the night!"

"There's a moon. Luke, we can do this!"

So we set to work with shovels and a barrow, filling in the holes and flattening the grass. The church clock was striking six when we patted down the last mole-hill, and my whole body felt as if it was on fire. I was so tired I would have fallen down, but Luke's arm crept round my waist and held me upright.

At that moment the front door opened and Lord Hareham strode down the marble steps. When he caught sight of our bedraggled figures still clutching shovels, his mouth fell open in surprise.

"Strangeways . . . Bessie. What the devil is going on?"

"Moles, sir," Luke said. "Dug up the croquet pitch. We've been up all night repairing it."

"Good heavens! How did you know what had happened?"

"The owls woke me, sir, and I saw the damage from my window," I said.

"We didn't want the guests to be disappointed," Luke added.

His Lordship smiled.

"I am fortunate indeed in my staff. Now, go straight to Mrs Bray and tell her she is to cook you both a breakfast of bacon, eggs and mushrooms, and anything else you desire. After that, you are to take the day off to rest."

"Thank you, sir, but we wouldn't want to miss the croquet," I chipped in, astounded at my own boldness.

"And I'd best be on hand in case of broken mallets or bent hoops, your Lordship," Luke added artfully.

WHAT a grand occasion the croquet party was, with the ladies in all their finery and the gentlemen smoking cigars and tapping the balls through the hoops. Excited chatter filled the air.

"Excellent shot, Lavinia!"

"Straight through the hoop in one go, Aubrey. Bravo!"

Mrs Bray had worked wonders, and I lost count of the platefuls of sandwiches, pies, desserts, cakes and fruit that I carried out to lay on the trestle tables.

At last the guests took their leave, and it was then that Luke and I were summoned by Lord Hareham.

"He wants to see you in the summerhouse," the butler said disapprovingly. He shook his head. "It ain't proper, hobnobbing with the gentry."

But what did I care, with the sun shining and Luke holding my hand in his?

Lord Hareham looked cheerful, too.

"It has been a splendid afternoon, thanks to your tireless work, and I intend to reward your loyalty. You, Bessie, are promoted herewith to housekeeper's assistant, with an increase of two shillings a week."

I completely forgot myself in my excitement.

"No more cleaning out the ashes at five in the morning, or peeling potatoes in that freezing scullery!" I cried. "Why, bless you for your kindness, sir."

His Lordship looked pleased.

"A similar wage increase for you, Strangeways." He turned to Luke. "And promotion to groundsman, if you'll accept the job."

Luke beamed.

"That's most generous of you, sir, especially seeing as I've been in your service only a short while."

"Not at all," Lord Hareham insisted. "Now, is there anything else I can do for you two?"

The words were out before I could stop them.

"Only one thing, your Lordship. Might Luke and I be allowed a game of croquet now that the grand folks have left?"

* * * *

Never will I forget that wonderful game — the excitement of aiming the ball for the hoops, the thrill of playing where the gentry had so recently gathered, and Luke's tall figure by my side and his murmured words of encouragement and praise.

When we reached the seventh hoop he glanced round to check that we were all alone. Then came the moment I had been dreaming of all day long, as his arms drew me close and his lips met mine. The croquet lawn became our own little heaven on earth, so neither of us noticed his Lordship striding back through the shrubbery, carrying a ball that must have gone astray.

He stopped in his tracks and cleared his throat loudly.

"How's the game going, Strangeways?"

Even Luke was stuck for an answer this time.

"We were . . . I was . . . er, we were trying to see if the ball had cleared the hoop, sir."

"I see." There was a twinkle of amusement in his Lordship's eye. "And are you winning?"

"Oh, yes, sir," Luke said softly, his eyes meeting mine in a gaze so tender it took my breath away. "I certainly am." ■

The Proof Of The Pudding . . .

by Celia K. Andrew.

"AND did someone bring you an Easter bunny, as well as all these nice eggs?" Mrs Davies (she of the somewhat disapproving little rosebud mouth) asked my six-year-old charge, her youngest grandson.

"Oh, yes," Matthew replied brightly. "But he took it away again after he'd shown it to me."

His grandmother was a little taken aback.

"What do you mean, Matthew? Was the bunny meant for you?"

I knew what was coming and tried to steer the conversation away, but Matthew was still fascinated by the offering Titus had brought him on Easter morning and wasn't about to give up.

"Cats do that, you know. Bring you presents. It makes them think they're the man of the family and can feed all their children."

Mrs Davies gave a horrified gasp and her hand flew up to cover her red rosebud lips in melodrama queen fashion.

"How horrid," she said, sitting down on the sofa. I half expected her to pull out a bottle of smelling salts, but she just gave me one of her looks instead. "I think you and I need a little chat, Clare."

* * * *

"It wasn't just the fact that the cat killed the rabbit and brought it into the house in the first place," she explained later. "It was the fact that Matt wasn't even disgusted or horrified by it. A little boy of his age shouldn't have to see dead things like that."

I didn't think that it was quite the moment to enlighten Mrs Davies about the immediate aftermath of the incident. Marian, aged twelve, had wept for a few minutes and then she and her brother had decided that a funeral would be a good idea.

The two of them had pored over hymn-books and prayers and arranged an Order of Service, and then all three of us had progressed down the garden and buried the wild rabbit under the cherry trees with a lovely ceremony.

"It's horrible," Mrs Davies finished.

"It's life," I said.

"Death, more like."

"Matthew and Marian live on a farm now. They see birth and death all the time. They know what happens to the lambs come the summer. And they know what the kestrel is up to when it's hovering so showily. They're very well adjusted to all that happens around them."

"Well," she replied, rather sniffily, "I hope you cleaned the floor thoroughly. You young girls are all the same, no idea about hygiene. Dead rabbits in the house! What would my daughter say?"

HER daughter, Helen, mother of the children, had married my cousin Don six months ago. They'd moved here to live in our village and they were getting on fine. And now Helen and my cousin had gone off on holiday for two weeks — a belated honeymoon — leaving me in charge of the children, the smallholding, the house, ponies, pets

Illustrations by Mike Heslop.

and other hangers-on.

Unfortunately, Mrs Davies, Helen's mother, had pitched up this morning from Surbiton with a suitcase in each hand and the intention of staying until the holidaymakers returned. And that was five whole days away.

Interestingly, the children had scarpered when they realised she was staying for a few days. Matt was at the Easter egg hunt on the village green and Marian had gone to a friend's house.

Mrs Davies was tutting to herself all the way up the stairs behind me as I took her to her room. Thank goodness the guest bedroom hadn't been used for weeks and was at least tidy! She sniffed as she went in, prodded the bed as though it were a heifer she was buying and walked over to the window.

"What a lovely view — you can see right across to Wales!"

"It's wonderful, isn't it?" At least we agreed on something!

"Although, the windows are a bit grubby. I think you and I might have a bit of a spring-clean, Clare. Make the place all spruce for Helen and Don coming home?"

I didn't like to say that the windows hadn't been cleaned for nearly a year. Don had told me that himself and Helen had just laughed. She, like Don, knew there were more important things in life than sparkling clean windows.

"And that old cooker looks as though it could do with a clean, too. And the bathroom I used downstairs."

We spent the rest of Easter Monday cleaning everything Mrs Davies could reach or get me to reach. I'm thirty years younger than she is and I was struggling to keep up. We did all the windows, inside and out, both bathrooms, the cooker, the kitchen floor and the back doorstep. Everything was dusted and wiped and scrubbed and, by five o'clock, I was sure Don wouldn't have recognised his own house.

"I'll leave you to do the pets' cages, Clare, while I make supper. We'll have that nice shepherd's pie I brought down with me . . ."

OR we would have done, if the dog hadn't already had it. Mrs Davies had left her shepherd's pie on the kitchen table and Bonzer had seen his chance. He was banished to an outhouse at her insistence after that and we ended up having frozen meals reheated in the Aga. The children were delighted.

"I love supermarket curries," Matt declared when he'd finished eating.

Realising that he was about to lick the plate clean, I jumped up and took it from him.

"Let me clear away and then we can have some of your grandma's apple crumble."

"It's the best in Surrey," she said and the rosebud opened a little into a smile.

"We're in Devon now, Grandma," Matt pointed out. "And Clare makes a mean apple crumble herself."

I could see I was going to have to say something or Matt's grandma was never going to feel part of the family again.

"No, Grandma's is best," I said firmly. "She's had more practice. Now, do you want custard or cream, Mrs Davies?"

I offered her the first bowl of crumble.

"Ice-cream," the children cried together.

"Manners!" The reproof was instant. "You weren't offered ice-cream."

"Oh, that's OK, they know there's loads." I tried to cover up for them, but quickly realised that that had been the wrong move.

"How can I insist on good manners if you undermine me, Clare?" The rosebud mouth tightened again and an embarrassed silence fell until Marian came back with the tub of ice-cream.

"Here, you've got to taste this . . ." Marian opened the tub, but her grip on the wet plastic container slipped and it hit her grandma's bowl of crumble on the table, which ended up in the Harris tweed lap.

Then we all watched, horrified, as the contents of the ice-cream container followed and landed on top of the splattered apple crumble.

Matthew whooped, grabbed his spoon and his bowl and made a dive for the mess. Marian, red-faced and mortified, patted ineffectively at her grandmother's skirt with a napkin and I just closed my eyes and hoped for divine intervention. What more could go wrong?

Mrs Davies, to give her credit, wasn't fazed in the least. In one swift movement, she returned the solidly frozen ice-cream from her lap to its container on the table. I could see that she was shaking and held my breath, wondering what was coming next.

Sound finally erupted from the rosebud mouth. And it was laughter. Bubbly, infectious, tear-inducing laughter. The rosebud opened into full bloom and the eyes above it were sparkling brightly with tears.

Marian and Matthew were both laughing as well now, and the three of them scraped apple crumble off her skirt and back into her bowl.

"Come on, Clare, bring your spoon and help yourself to ice-cream," Mrs Davies suggested. "I shall have this one."

She pulled the crumble basin towards her with the crusty-edge remains of the crumble in it and dolloped some ice-cream into the middle of it.

"Cook's prerogative — all the crunchy bits," she announced and actually winked at me as she started to eat.

THE previously stilted atmosphere had completely evaporated. We sat round the table and demolished the remains of the meal in hilarious merriment. Marian got up, unasked, and made a pot of tea and served it in the Easter mugs her grandmother had brought for us.

"Cool mugs, Grandma," Matthew said, slurping. He flicked a glance at me and then apologised to Mrs Davies of his own accord.

"The toffee eggs are wicked, too," Marian added. "Nice change from chocolate." The kids were really trying to include her now, and the effort was touching.

"Do you want to come and see the falconer flying the Harris hawk tomorrow, Grandma? He's going to do a display on the green at eleven."

"And then you can come and visit the Ice-cream Farm open day," Matthew declared. "And we can get some yummy honeycomb crunch for tea instead of this boring old vanilla . . ."

"Didn't hear you complaining a few minutes ago," his sister muttered.

Somehow, instead of looking like a nightmare, the next few days were being booked up with places to go and things to see — things that the children wanted to share with their grandmother. My input wasn't really needed; the ice had been broken, quite literally, with the flying ice-cream carton.

BUT Mrs Davies had one final surprise in store for me.

After the children had gone to bed that night, she suddenly turned to me.

"Thank you, Clare," she said.

"For what?"

"For not laughing first, at suppertime, when we had the incident with the pudding. For letting me be the one to start the laughter, the joke against myself. I must confess that I was feeling very much an outsider earlier today. It just seemed that this new life of theirs had no place for a Surrey grandmother. All I could do and say was find fault, digging myself deeper and deeper into the disapproving granny mould. You helped me find a way out."

I really didn't know what to say. It had been shock — and tact — on my part that had held me back, rather than anything more definite, but I had to admit that her frankness was rather endearing.

I smiled at her and she smiled back and there was a definite twinkle in her blue eyes now.

"Please, Clare, do call me June. Mrs Davies sounds so very formal and we are family, after all. Exactly what relation are you to me, do you think? Step cousin-once-removed-in-law?"

We both laughed out loud at that one and I leaned across and poured her another cup of tea.

And then June rounded things off rather neatly by adding, "We've done quite enough cleaning and tidying for one holiday, Clare. Tomorrow, how about you and the children start teaching me all about this country life in Devon?"

"That sounds perfect. I can't wait," I said, and really meant it. ■

Next Stop Romance!

by Liz Gilbey.

ONE day I'm going to learn to drive a car. I frequently tell myself this, usually when standing at the bus stop on a cold, wet and blustery day — like today — getting soaked! Normally I'm the only person waiting for the early bus, but this morning Jane Lawson, my next-door neighbour, is standing with her three children. Her car won't start and they are due at the dentist, so the five of us crowd on to the tiny square beneath the shelter.

We are so busy trying to keep dry and shelter the children with our umbrellas that we don't notice a man running along the road until almost too late. Lee, Sam and Ruby tug our arms and shout, "Look out!"

Illustration by Gaeta.

Then we see him. A muscular, sun-tanned vision in singlet and shorts. He has his head down against the rain as he runs and we try to step out of his way.

Just as we do so, he looks up, spots us, and takes avoiding action, too. Somehow we all end up thrown together in a heap at the back of the bus shelter and I find myself clutching a hard, damp masculine body to stop both of us falling over.

"Ooof!" he exclaims.

We are eyeball to eyeball, clasped more tightly together than dancing a waltz. His eyes, I notice appreciatively, are speedwell-blue. He is rather dishy and he smells of rain and fresh air.

"This is no way to meet a gorgeous girl!" he says, laughing and steadying me by the elbows.

"You're standing on my foot!" Lee squeaks with eight-year-old indignation. And so, a potentially romantic meeting in the rain turns into a comedy of errors.

So the gorgeous bloke lets me go, apologises for treading on us, rescues my umbrella from the gutter and hands it back to me with a bow. Just like you see in old films!

"Your umbrella," he says. "Wish I'd brought one with me!"

"It would be hard work to hold in this rain," I say primly. "Have you run far?"

He laughs out loud.

"From Starmore. It was sunny when I started! I'm training for a charity run."

"You'd be better off on the bus on a day like this," I reply tartly. Because I don't want to look as smitten as I feel!

At that moment the bus arrives. Jane, her children and I get on, leaving our runner standing on the kerb, waving us goodbye. This memory keeps me smiling all the way into work.

NEXT morning I almost forget about him, until I board my bus and he is there, sitting behind the driver, smiling at me. He looks different in a grey suit, with a trendy man bag.

"Hello! I didn't think you would recognise me," he says, sliding along the double seat so I can join him.

But I sit just behind. I'm not the sort of girl to share a seat with a stranger. Even if he is gorgeous!

"No problem," I say. "It's the sticky-out ears that give you away."

He laughs, turns in his seat, holds out his hand.

"Dale Harrington," he says. "Pleased to meet you."

"Casey Nicholls," I reply, taking his hand briefly. "Likewise."

During the journey, he explains that he has just moved to Starmore, and his charity run is in three weeks. And that he got very wet yesterday!

"You would have been dry on the bus," I remark.

"I'm not running eight miles into work, thanks." He laughs. "You don't drive to work, then?"

"No need!" I say airily, ignoring my ambitions about learning to drive and getting a car.

"That's good," he agrees, still smiling.

Oh, I like that smile! And I'd like to see it again. I tell him I've lived at Westerby Hilltop all my life, always worked in Westrill and that I cycled into

Tawny Owl

THE tawny owl hunts mainly at night and watches from a perch before dropping down silently on its victim. They eat a variety of prey, but woodland rodents, birds, earthworms and beetles make up the majority of their diet.

Inhabiting forests and sometimes mature conifer plantations, the tawny owl prefers to live close to water. Gardens, parks and cemeteries have meant that it can live in quite urban areas and you might have heard the distinctive mating call — hoo-hoo-hoo — as you went about your business.

Tawny owls are monogamous and usually pair off at the age of one year. They typically nest in a hole in a tree or building, but will take to nest boxes if provided. The tawny owl fiercely defends its young and will patrol its territory relentlessly. People, or dogs and cats, who have strayed too close to the nest are liable to be attacked with sharp talons.

Its sharp hearing, ten times more effective than a human being's, means that the tawny owl can hunt in complete darkness using this sense only. The sound of raindrops makes it difficult to detect faint sounds, however, and tawny owls have been known to starve to death in periods of prolonged wet weather.

Wildstock.

work — once — when I missed the bus.

To make him laugh I tell funny stories about bicycle rides and punctures. I prattle away because he's gorgeous and I like to watch him laugh. But we are suddenly at my stop and I have to wave goodbye.

Thinkstockphotos.

* * * *

Dale is on the bus the next day, too. So I give him a season ticket application form.

"Being new, I thought you might not know about the bus company's services," I explain.

"Thanks, Casey. I don't know what to say."

He looks flustered. Perhaps he isn't used to people being helpful. So I explain about special discounts for holiday travel, day trips and stuff. Then it's time to leave him before I know it — the journey to work has never seemed as short as this before.

BY Thursday morning we are beginning to share information about ourselves when Rachel Steed gets on the bus. She and I were at school together. She's tall, confident and clever — all the things I'm not. She comes and joins us.

"Hi, Casey. I haven't seen you for ages, how are you? Who's your friend?"

She flashes her super-strength smile in Dale's direction. Dale smiles back and I introduce them.

"So why are you on the bus?" she asks.

"Keeping Casey company," he replies gallantly, blushing a little.

I suddenly realise that Dale might be shy, especially when faced with an extrovert like Rachel!

"Too bad!" Rachel commiserates, twinkling at him.

I'm so annoyed by her blatant appreciation of my new friend I say, "He doesn't have to, he's just kind. Anyway, I'm catching an earlier bus next week, so he'll have a break. I'm deputising for my boss and will need to be in early to open up."

Signs Of Spring

THE first warmth of the sun caresses the land,
And winter retracts his hoar-frosted hand,
The days start to lengthen, the soil blessed with rain,
Buds on the branches are growing again.

Animals emerge from their winter-long sleep,
The hedgehog from under the cold compost heap,
The catkins are dangling, the pussy willow purrs,
And all of Creation finally stirs.

The daffs and the crocus come up through the ground,
Birdsong fills up the woodland with sound.
Spring has arrived, a time of rebirth,
As God blesses all living things on this Earth.

— Antony Burr.

"You didn't tell me," Dale says.

"So poor Dale will be travelling on his own." Rachel laughs. "Well, my car will be fixed tomorrow so perhaps I can offer him a lift instead? I'd hate to think of him being lonely."

"Thanks, but I won't need a lift," Dale replies.

"Shame!" Rachel flutters her eyelashes at him.

Which is when Rachel and I leave the bus at the same stop.

"See you the week after next!" Dale calls after me.

I nod and wave and realise how much I'm going to miss my new travelling companion. I decide that when I'm back on my normal bus again — and with Dale — I'll ask him about his hobbies and whether he has a girlfriend. But my plans are ruined before they begin.

"Sorry about this, Casey," my boss greets me. "But I'm not going into hospital for my operation after all. The surgeon has flu and my wisdom tooth has to wait."

I'm delighted. It means I will see Dale again even sooner than I had expected.

* * * *

On Monday I hop aboard the bus, smiling and looking for Dale. But he isn't there! Not even on the top deck. I can't believe it. Perhaps he's missed the bus or he's ill.

Feeling oddly deflated without him there, I do what I always used to do when on the bus alone. I take out my book and read. But the pages keep blurring as I think about Dale.

He's not on the bus on Tuesday. I look out for him, in case he has training runs past my house, but there is no sign. On Wednesday morning I finish my book and sit with it on my lap. I'm looking absently out of the window when something catches my eye.

A small silver car is alongside the bus at traffic lights. There is something a bit familiar — in fact, very familiar — about the driver's profile. Surely — surely it can't be Dale? I sit bolt upright and rap on the bus window, but he doesn't hear me.

Then the car pulls away, leaving the bus behind. I am bewildered.

* * * *

On Thursday morning I am ready, looking out the bus window at every car. The silver car flashes by on the dual carriageway, and I am certain the driver is Dale! I wonder why he has never mentioned a car or even being able to drive.

On Friday morning, I spot the silver car again at traffic lights. In fact, I move forward three seats to see properly. Moving catches the driver's eye. In that instant Dale and I look at each other. He recognises me and turns bright red!

He mouths something, shakes his head, but I can't understand him, and I turn away. He has a car and can drive to work — yet he let me prattle on about bicycles, buses and season tickets. And why did he travel on the bus all last week?

I make up my mind to forget about him — and I try hard. All weekend, in fact, though not very successfully.

WHEN I get on the bus on Monday morning Dale is back sitting in the usual seat, as if waiting for me. He smiles brightly and I give a non-committal little nod. Though he shifts along the seat to make room for me, I sit behind, as I had that very first morning we travelled together.

"Morning, Casey. Have a good weekend?"

"Shouldn't you ask if I had a good week at work standing in for my manager?" I reply. "Or did you realise, when you saw me on Friday, that I hadn't been travelling on an earlier bus at all? Nice car, by the way."

He has the grace to look sheepish.

"Something like that," he agrees.

"Why didn't you tell me you had a car?" I ask, trying not to sound hurt. "What were you doing on the bus anyway?"

He is about to answer when the bus stops and Rachel gets on again.

"Hi, Dale, hi, Casey," she greets us, sitting down next to Dale as if he were an old friend.

"Car still broken?" Dale asks sympathetically.

"It's taking ages," Rachel says, clearly vexed. "So I'm back on the bus."

She turns to Dale.

"But what about you?" she asks. "I saw you driving into town last week. So why are you on the bus?"

Dale shrugs his shoulders in an embarrassed way.

"Like I said before, keeping Casey company."

He looks at me and my heart gives a little flip. I gasp. Was this really romance on the early bus?

Rachel looks from Dale to me and back again.

"Oh, it's like that, is it?" she asks, laughing. "You two dear, sweet, old-fashioned things!" she exclaims. "Too shy to admit you've taken a fancy to each other. Is that because you met in such an old-fashioned way? Travelling on a bus?"

"We met at a bus stop, actually," I correct primly.

Both Rachel and Dale laugh out loud at that!

"Yes, I can see that makes a difference," Rachel says, trying hard to be serious.

"I tripped over, fell head first into her arms and head over heels in love," Dale admits.

I LOOK at him, shocked. Did he really mean that?

I gaze at Dale, and Dale gazes at me. We are both blushing, not knowing whether to laugh or curl up with embarrassment at Rachel's accurate assessment.

"Go on, then, ask her out!" Rachel urges.

Dale looks from her to me, then takes a deep breath.

"Casey, will you come out with me? Please? I only left my car at home and travelled on the bus in the first place so I could get to know you. And I would have asked you out before now if it hadn't been for your enthusiasm for bicycles and bus travel. I thought you were some sort of environmental activist. Very green! I didn't dare admit I drive a sports car and sell cars for a living . . ."

"I suppose I am green, in a way," I agree. "But I'm not about to turn down a date with a lovely guy because he doesn't have a bus pass! Thank you, Dale. I would love to come out with you."

"Call me Cupid!" Rachel laughs. "I'd better get to work now I've done my good deed for the day!"

She stands up and presses the bell, and she's still smiling as she gets off the bus.

I, meanwhile, stay on the bus past my usual stop. Well, Dale and I have lots to say to each other — and a date to arrange. ■

St George And The Dragon

If George was my knight in shining armour, what, then, did that make Miss Aggie?

THE sun is sinking low over the horizon, spilling violet-gold rays over the roofs and chimney pots of Honey Dew Farm, where I work as personal maid to its mistress, Miss Agatha Brownlow. A large, imposing country residence nestling deep in the valley carved between the limestone hills of this hidden heart of England, it's a truly beautiful place and I'm the luckiest girl in the world to have found employment here.

I sigh — a little wistfully, perhaps, for one so young, or maybe simply because I *am* so young — taking a moment from my work to gaze fretfully out of the window towards the barn where there's such great and unexpected activity none would believe it.

If only my day's work were done and I was with the rest of the young folk having such fun.

It's all at the instigation of my master, the best and kindest master in the world, who says 'tis only right the ancient tradition of the Mummers' Play should be revived and the clothes and props be dug out of the old wardrobe up in the attics.

Once upon a time, it's said, such jollities were common here at the farm, not only to welcome in the spring and bring luck to the year's planting, but also in celebration of another winter survived.

Illustration by David McAllister.

And there's none can deny that the one just past has taken some surviving. Even my mistress, the most fractious and exacting mistress ever to be found, has had to agree that the turn of the century has been accompanied by a winter so cold there's been none like it in living memory, freezing the rivers and brooks, and even the poor ducks to the surface of the millpond, so that we all had to help release the poor things.

Such a survival deserves celebrating, Master says, though we know his game, old romantic that he is. No doubt he has an eye to another tradition following on from the play, that every young man in the employ of the farm should present a rose plucked from the master's own garden to the young girl of his choice . . .

* * * *

I've finished embroidering Miss Aggie's pretty lace hankie, and look lovingly at the bright red cross I've newly stitched to the tunic of a handsome young farm hand by the name of George Fairbrother. St George being not only the patron saint of England but in particular of farmers and fieldworkers, what else should the play be but an enactment of St George and the dragon?

by Sally Wragg.

And who else, given that he shares the same name, must play the part of the gentle knight but our very own George?

I can imagine his broad-shouldered frame filling the tunic, his fine bright eyes gazing down into mine with a wondering mixture of hope and desire . . .

But it isn't only imagination, I remind myself. I know George likes me; I can tell by the way his eyes follow me. And I like him, so surely, given the occasion, something must come of it?

And if there are those who say George has been spooning after Sarah Pickering, sadly and, in my humble opinion, misguidedly chosen by Master as damsel in distress for the festivities, and who comes up daily from the village to work in the dairy . . . well, I'd like to see those who'd say it to my face!

"Rosamond Albright, I do believe you've taken leave of your senses."

The sharp voice jolts me out of my reverie so that I jump, startled, and prick my finger. I find my hankie and bandage it hastily lest I mark George's fine tunic. Miss Aggie, who has been dozing in her favourite place in the armchair by the window, has woken and, seeing what I'm up to, reaches for her walking stick, banging it sharply on the floor in front of her.

"Wasting time on such a ridiculousness . . ."

"Oh, but, Miss Aggie, it isn't! The master says . . ."

"Never you mind the master! He has no more sense than the day he was born!"

Poor old lady, it must be her arthritis that's making her even more ill-tempered than usual. I break the thread between my teeth and shake the tunic out before carefully refolding it. The best way, the only way, to deal with Miss Aggie, the master says, is to stand up to her.

"It's a great shame I haven't mastered the art of it yet," he'll add, his rheumy old eyes twinkling.

"Shall I heat your milk, Miss Aggie?" I ask, hoping to chivvy her into a good mood.

"Need you ask?" she answers irritably. "And don't dawdle about it," she calls as I head for the door, her attention taken by George's tunic, folded neatly over my arm. It's as if she guesses I mean to take a detour via the barn on my way down to the kitchen.

"YOU'VE made a wonderful job of it, Rosamond. Thank you!" George beams, taking the tunic and holding it up for inspection.

The barn is a hive of bustling activity, folk painting the stage and trying on costumes with good-natured raillery, and all suffused with a sense of urgency. Time is rushing on. The play's tomorrow, St George's Day, and I feel a thrill of pleasure I try, if unsuccessfully, to conceal. It wouldn't do for George to guess the way I feel, though neither would it help if he didn't guess at all! I can only puzzle at how complicated life is.

"'Tis nothing, George," I respond shyly.

"Aye, there's nothing to beat a pair of pretty blue eyes, young George," the dragon says, lumbering past and treating my would-be swain to a friendly slap on the back. But truly it's not a beast to instil much fear into a mortal's heart, for my master's amiable face is plainly visible through its gaping mouth.

George colours up, but he dons the tunic happily and, seizing his broadsword, duels an imaginary foe, though he soon has to give it up to wipe the tears of mirth from his eyes.

"Oh, Rosamond, I fear I shall make a poor knight," he protests.

What can I say? I, who think him the best, the handsomest St George in the world!

"Oh, but you'll manage wonderfully!" I respond, perhaps a little too heartily.

I have the feeling he wants to say something, if only he knew quite how to say it, and my heart skips a beat. He does like me, I know he does, but he has always been shy, especially around us girls. Add into this happy mix that I'm not exactly forthcoming, and we could be playing this game of will he, won't he for ever.

"Coming to join the rehearsals, George?"

Wretchedly, just when I think we might be getting somewhere, I see Sarah Pickering approaching and laying possessive claim to George's arm, while treating me to a cool stare which clearly tells me a battle line has been drawn. I know she has always liked George and I am sure she means to get him for herself.

Laughing and triumphant, she leads him away and I take what comfort I can from the regretful look he throws me over his shoulder.

If I delay much longer Miss Aggie will have my guts for garters, so I leave them to their rehearsal and hurry away to the rest of my evening, dealing with my mistress's frequent and fractious demands.

I'm more than usually clumsy, spilling her bedtime milk and snagging her hair when I pin it up in paper so that she demands to know if I mean to separate it from her scalp.

I'm glad to escape to bed, where I dream of George, saving me from the clutches of a dreadful, fire-eating dragon too like my mistress for comfort.

I WAKE to broad daylight and my mistress's voice demanding her tea and some time this morning if I've a mind to it. I've overslept!

I quickly dress and run downstairs for the tea, which I slop in the saucer, and then, worse, slop over the bedcovers when I place it on her bedside table.

"What a clumsy!" she scolds.

I'm surprised she's so restrained, but then, when she eases herself out of bed and I see how she struggles to pull on her dressing-gown with her arthritic fingers, I feel nothing but sorrow and understanding as to what makes her so ill-tempered.

I run her bath whilst she hobbles downstairs to the master, intent on catching him on some business or other before he begins his day's work. I suspect she wants to tell him what a fool he is, wasting time on the Mummers' Play, for I know full well her opinion on the matter.

As the taps from the master's new-fangled water system run into the bath in the little annexe off her room, I wander back into the bedroom, staring dreamily out of the window and imagining the evening to come which, thwarted in love or not, is still bound to be an exciting one. I can just see the handsome young knight, my wonderful George, astride his pure white charger, in reality Master's own best hunter, skewering the damsel-eating monster.

Uncharitably I wonder if it mightn't be better to let the dragon win this time. That would sort out Miss Sarah Pickering!

A prescience of danger brings me spinning back to the present — though horribly too late. My hand flies to my mouth to stifle the scream at the sight greeting me through the doorway into the bathroom.

The taps are still running merrily, water even now cascading over the edge of the bath and seeping over the floor and carpet. But how can I have been daydreaming long enough for such a calamity to have happened? Worse, my mistress has returned, her shock mirroring my own when she sees what I've done.

"Turn off the taps! Turn off the taps!" she screeches, and at last I catapult into action.

The next long and wretched moments are filled with mopping up and explanations and even more explanations when the master rushes in, brought from downstairs at the sight of the large stain on the dining-room ceiling, directly beneath the bathroom.

There are no explanations worthy, no apologies hearty enough.

"If you think for one moment you'll be going to any play after this . . ." Miss Aggie rails.

"Mother, have a heart," my master pleads, soft-hearted as ever.

"It isn't as if this is her first misdemeanour of late," she exclaims irritably. "The girl's head is in the clouds. I told you no good would come of all this silly mummery business. She shall stay up here with me and that shall be an end to it!"

That I won't even be around for George to present his rose after the play doesn't bear thinking about.

"Rosamond, I'm sorry. Mayhap she'll let you slip down some time later?" my master says quietly when Miss Aggie turns away.

We both know that for the untruth it is, but it's not this dear man's fault, so I smile and say I'm sure she will.

"POOR you," Sarah says, gloating, not even taking the trouble to hide her delight.

We're at lunch, taken by the servants together in the servants' hall. I push my plate away, my appetite quite gone.

By my own carelessness, I've left the way clear for Sarah. If only George could see through her, but, as usual, she is all sweetness and light where he is concerned.

Holyroodhouse

RIGHT in the heart of the city of Edinburgh, the Palace of Holyroodhouse is situated at the end of the Royal Mile, and is the Queen's official residence in Scotland. It's certainly had a turbulent past, with previous occupants including Mary, Queen of Scots, but nowadays the palace is the setting for State ceremonies and official entertaining, including the famous garden parties, which were first held by King George V and Queen Mary.

George, as it happens, is sitting next to her and across from me.

"Rosamond, I'm so sorry," he says softly, looking as if he truly means it so that for a moment some of my misery lifts.

When he leaves the table, Sarah in hot pursuit, the look he gives me suggests he's even sorrier than I am, and what am I to make of that other than that he feels for me what I feel for him? Oh, if only he did and if only it wasn't just hopeful imagination!

All around is barely subdued anticipation. As the day progresses, I drag the enormity of my punishment around with me. Yet I am determined to put a brave face on it, concentrating on the jobs in hand, changing my mistress's bed linen, sorting clothes, darning and mending, carrying out her every order, sometimes before she's even issued it. Despite my misdemeanours, at least it appears I'm earning her grudging admiration.

We're in the garden where she likes to walk and see the flowers my dear master has planted especially for her. We come to a halt by a strangely denuded rose bush. I have a hold of her arm, and I can't help turning to her in remorse.

"Oh, Miss Aggie, I'm so sorry!" I say contritely.

"And so you should be!" she snaps, thumping her stick to the ground.

That the response is so sharp when I'd detected a mellowing is too much to bear. To my horror I'm on the verge of tears.

"It's just so hard to miss the play!" I wail.

"You've none to blame but yourself," she points out.

She has no need to tell me. This time the tears fall for real, and for a moment I can't speak.

"Pull yourself together, child," she says crossly, finding her hankie and thrusting it towards me. "Mayhap I'll allow you downstairs later — but only for a moment or two, mind!" she adds as if she instantly regrets her show of leniency.

Oh, but to see even a little and when I'd thought to see nothing! Wild hope leaps into my heart, but my mistress says no more, and I don't care to press things in case I press too far.

WE return to our rooms. Evening is fast approaching and it's cruel to hear the hustle and bustle, the chatter and laughter and slamming of doors as actors and audience alike head towards the barn, from which direction shortly I hear applause. To my misery, the play has begun without me.

I look towards the farm's mistress hopefully, but all she says — and sharply, to boot — is to fetch her book and, as is usual at this time of our evening, to sit and read to her.

There is nothing else for it but to do as she asks and begin to read in a tear-filled voice.

As usual, though it's a thing she always denies, her eyes close and her head nods forward, and her ladylike snores intersperse with the shouts and cheers drifting from the barn.

There's no denying my mistress is impossible and has a temper everyone fears, even my master, but for all that she's honest and never says a thing she doesn't mean. And I know she meant to allow me to see at least a little of the play, even if it's now likely to end before she's aware of it.

Desperation rises. I cough and cough, vainly hoping this will wake her. Must I shake her?

I resist, instead hastening to the window to look hopelessly out. The applause is reaching a crescendo and if I don't go soon I know it will be too late.

The stern old lady behind me, who would have made a better dragon by far than her son, is likely to be mortified when she wakes and realises. Worse, she'll be cross that I never woke her. As if I'd dare do such a thing!

IT'S impulse, if not a madness brought to life by my growing desperation, but before I have a chance to stop myself, I'm running down the stairs and across the yard.

I slip into the back of the barn just as a splendidly handsome St George draws his sword and plunges it into the heart of such a pitiful-looking dragon that everyone appears more sorrowful than anything else.

Though I thrill at it, I don't much enjoy what follows, as the knight strides the stage to cut the damsel's bonds and, to a rousing cheer, folds her into his arms. Sarah takes full advantage, leaning back and looking up at her rescuer so longingly that I want to slap her.

Still, I've seen something of the events and give as great a cheer as any as the amiable old dragon miraculously comes back to life in time to take a bow with the rest of the cast.

It's impossible to think that I must miss the presentation of roses and the dance following, but I accept that I must retire gracefully and, when my mistress awakes, tell her what I have done. She will understand . . . She's bound to understand, isn't she?

For the first time, a tiny niggle of doubt stirs. Mayhap she won't be quite as understanding as I anticipate. Is that why I look backstage before I depart? As if I might take some courage from it?

As soon as I do, I wish I hadn't, for I see a thing I can't bear. George, no doubt assuming me absent, has a hold of Sarah's hand and, fingering the red rose pinned to his chest, is gazing deeply into her eyes for all the world like any young man in love and about to declare his intentions . . .

"There you are, lady!" A sharp voice barks behind me, and involuntarily I cry out, causing heads to turn amongst the folk nearby.

The very worst of catastrophes has happened: my mistress has wakened and, finding me gone, come straight here, determined, I see by her face, to give me the dressing-down of all dressing-downs.

Perhaps, heaven forbid, she even means to pay me off rather than have in her employ one so blatantly untrustworthy.

My eyes screwed tight shut, I wretchedly wait for retribution to rain down on my unprotected head.

There's an agonising pause, during which absolutely nothing happens. The silence is deafening.

I crack open one eye, then the other, and am shocked to see George, in courtly manner in keeping with his costume, bowing before my mistress. A little burgeoning hope springs up.

There are more ways to defeat a dragon than by the sword, it would appear.

Thinkstockphotos.

To the surprise and delight of all around, George quickly unpins the rose from his tunic and, kneeling, offers it up to her.

What can she do? Who could resist? Hesitating barely a moment and to a smattering of applause, she accepts the gift with grace.

It's a touching scene, and the fact that George has engineered it in order to save me should warm me through.

It doesn't, though, because I can't forget what's gone before — and, worse still, even now I see Sarah weaving her sultry way through the crowd towards us.

I **STILL** have some wits left. Pushing heedlessly through the throng, I make my escape, stumbling towards the garden where there's a modicum of privacy in which to attempt to make some sense of my wildly raging feelings.

I'm in love, but thwarted love was never meant to be the final scene of the mummery!

Spring In Kintail

THE Sisters wear their veils of cloud,
A lonely cuckoo calls,
And rustling mountain streams are loud
With songs of waterfalls.

The rowan at the cottage door
Is dressed in creamy lace,
And sunlight warms the stony shore,
And gilds the sea-loch's face.

The castle on the Otter's Isle
A fairy fortress seems.
The fairest scene for many a mile,
It lingers in our dreams.

And when the day is growing old,
A sight to charm the eye,
The Cuillin peaks all edged with gold,
Against the western sky.

— Brenda G. Macrow.

"Rosamond! Please . . . What's the matter?" George has followed me. Does he mean to mock me? To be so uncaring of the hurt he inflicts? I'd never have thought it of him!

Gently he takes my arm, pulling me round towards him, upset when I resist.

"Miss Aggie isn't so very cross," he insists, "though I dare say you'll have another ticking off to endure . . ."

My ever-sensible, sensitive knight must see by my expression that this isn't the problem, and his face falls in consternation. And then, rather wonderfully, I see a dawning comprehension. He frowns, speaking urgently.

"Rosamond, you mustn't think Sarah means a thing to me. I'm no fool! I know she's been making eyes at me. I was only telling her I am already intended . . . or . . . rather, that I would like to be intended."

He colours up, my dear George, as shy and unassuming as ever despite his valour.

His words are such balm, I can't take them in. He sees it and a slow, bright smile lights his face. He has to convince me and I see now he's spied exactly the way to do it.

ON the bush to the side of the path is a single stem bearing a rose, deep dark red in colour, the evening dew already gathering around its drooping petals.

Uncaring of the scratches he receives for his pains, George reaches out and breaks it off.

"A rose for a rose," he murmurs, kneeling and raising it up in his two cupped hands towards me.

What else can I do? My knight has vanquished more than one dragon in this night's work.

I take the velvet-red rose with a soft little sigh of happiness as he springs up and gathers me into his arms. ■

by Angela Pickering.

The Floral Dance

"STOP that!"

Will's heart jumped up into his throat. His mind had been miles away whilst his hands seemed to do the weeding by themselves. The young woman with the loud voice glared at him from over the low brick wall of his front garden. His mouth dropped open as he realised how pretty she was, and how very, very annoyed.

The silence between them seemed to stretch for hours before he recovered his wits and lurched to his feet, still clutching the results of his weeding efforts.

"Oh, no," the girl wailed, looking at the contents of his hands.

"They're only weeds," he said. "I'm tidying up the garden."

"They're not weeds," she grumbled, giving him a fierce look. "They're poppies, Californian poppies."

Will glanced down at the strangling mass of greenery cascading through his fingers.

"Oh," he said, feeling a sudden, ridiculous urge to apologise to this strange girl. "They look like weeds to me."

"You should be more careful," the girl snarled. "Find out what you're doing before you pull stuff up all over the place."

Will felt the first stirrings of irritation himself.

"Hang on a minute," he said. "This is my garden, you know."

His annoyance faded abruptly as he saw tears sparkling in the dark blue eyes of the girl. She brushed at them with the back of a hand and then, without a word, strode away down the road.

WELL, what do you make of that?" Will said out loud. He threw the poppies into the pile he had already collected in his wheelbarrow. He was going to have a compost heap in the back garden and had already made a good start on it.

He stretched, both hands on the small of his back, and groaned. A hot bath was what was needed after such a busy evening in the garden. He inspected his handiwork.

Californian poppies, Will thought, noting the huge number that he hadn't yet pulled up. I might just leave them there and see what they're like.

Later, in the bath, he wondered about his strange encounter with the pretty, but peculiar, young woman. Will had only been in the village a short while and hadn't met many people. He had no idea who the girl might be or why she had been so upset with him.

The scented bath water began to untie the knots in his aching joints, and he found himself relaxing. His thoughts wandered over the last few months and the relationship that he had recently left.

He and Melanie had seemed perfect together at first and had become engaged within three months of their meeting. Neither of them had realised that they were moving too quickly. Will had bought the sweet little cottage in the village thinking it would be the perfect place for them to begin married life.

Mel had seemed to agree at first, but within days of the completion of the purchase, the cracks in their relationship had begun to show. More like crevasses than cracks, Will mused, sinking deeper into the bath water and remembering the rows they had had whilst discussing the silliest things, like what colour to decorate the lounge.

A lot of their problems had been his fault, he knew. Maybe he had been more in love with the idea of living happily ever after than he had been with the real human being that was Melanie. Before he knew it, the wedding was off and he was left with a mortgage and a dilapidated cottage. In many ways, he was relieved and thankful that he and Mel had come to their senses before they had invested any more time in one another. In the end, they had parted on good terms, neither one suffering from the dreaded broken heart, and both of them a touch wiser.

At least he still had the cottage, and since she had never lived there, he had no sad memories to spoil his enjoyment of it.

Will smiled and climbed out of the cooling water. Lots of good things had come from his time with Mel, he thought, not least of which was his appreciation of the joys of gardening.

The cottage was much nicer than his old flat in the city. Even the daily trek into work was worthwhile when he had his weekends and spring evenings to spend in his very own garden. He did realise, though, that if he was to be happy in his new home, he needed to make friends in the village. He'd do something about it, he decided, as soon as the garden was sorted.

The next morning was Saturday and Will's first task of the day was a visit to the local garden centre. The ancient assistant was quite amused by Will's query regarding Californian poppies.

"Aren't you the young fella who's just moved into Poppy Cottage?" he said, grinning.

"Yes, I am," Will said. "That's why I need to know about poppies, isn't it?"

"I'll call Tasha," the man replied. "She's our poppy expert."

"I might have known," Will said as the promised Tasha strolled over.

The gorgeous blue eyes were once again looking his way, this time without the sparks of annoyance.

"Hello again," she said in such a friendly way that Will, surprised, took an involuntary step backwards into a display of terracotta pots.

THE pots rolled everywhere and Will scampered through the shop trying to gather them up. The sound of laughter made him pause in his efforts and look up. His new acquaintance was obviously finding the situation highly amusing.

"First I make you cry, and now you're laughing at me," he said with a smile. "And we haven't even been introduced."

The laughter stopped and the girl held out her hand to him.

"I'm Tasha," she said. "I work here, and my grandmother used to own your cottage."

In those few words, Will felt as if Tasha had explained everything he needed to know.

"I see," he said, taking her hand. "That's why you were so upset about my weeding yesterday."

Tasha nodded.

"I am so sorry," she said. "Gran hasn't been gone all that long, and it seemed so strange to see someone else in her garden." She looked a little embarrassed. "Especially pulling up her flowers."

"I thought they were weeds, you know," Will said, finding himself reluctant to let go of her hand.

"Californian poppies are not weeds," she replied with a touch of her original fire. "They are the most beautiful flowers you could wish for, and they don't need much care, they just keep on growing."

"And you love them."

Tasha's expression softened.

"Oh, yes. And so did my dear gran."

"I'm Will," he said. "I need gardening advice."

"You certainly do." She finally gave him the smile he realised he'd been hoping for.

"Stop pulling up the poppies for a start. When they flower in the summer you'll fall in love with them."

"I hope so. There are still an awful lot of them."

She moved closer.

"THEY'RE magic poppies, you know," Tasha said, lowering her voice as if she were telling him an amazing secret. "They seed themselves and come up a different colour every time."

"So you never know what's going to come up?"

She nodded her head.

"A bit like life, really," she said. She looked at the ground for a moment and when she raised her face to his, Will could see a faint blush staining her cheeks.

"I do apologise for being so rude to you yesterday," she continued. "It's just that I miss my gran so much, and to see you doing that to her garden . . ."

"I understand," Will said, fighting the urge to take her hand again. "A different colour every time, you say?"

"Well, orange, yellow, cream, and the most beautiful shade of pink."

"Sounds wonderful," Will said, gazing into the most beautiful shade of blue. "Like life."

Tasha giggled, and the sound made Will's heart somersault yet again.

"You just have to be patient and wait until they flower," she said. "It'll be worth the wait."

Will nodded. He had learned lately that some things shouldn't be rushed.

"Would you like to help me gather up these pots?" he asked. "And then maybe you could help me buy a watering can."

"No plants?"

"No," Will replied. "Apparently I don't need any. I already have magic poppies in my garden." He smiled and crossed his fingers behind his back in hope. "Maybe you'd like to come and see them some time?" ■

A Piece Of Advice

MOLLY never expected to hear from Ronald again. They had met on a Greek Island cruise and, pardon the pun, Molly had thought they were simply ships that pass in the night. He had promised to write, but, well — you do, don't you? Jack had also said he would keep in touch, but there had been no word from him.

And now this letter from Ronald. What a surprise. A nice one, at that. Silly, too, that when she read his name on the back of the envelope Molly felt a little frisson.

Well, she may have been sixty-eight, but she was not yet past the odd flutter.

She and Ronald had got along from the start. He had been travelling alone while Molly holidayed with her closest and oldest friend, Bella. They had met Ronald and Jack, also on their own, the first day of the cruise and all four of them were good chums from the start. Ronald was a lovely dancer and the kind of gent she'd imagined had gone the way of Brylcreem and the Light Programme.

"Yep, a real charmer," Bella agreed that first evening, back in their cabin. "Good-looking, too — like Brad Pitt's dad."

"How do you know what Brad Pitt's dad looks like?" Molly asked with a wry smile.

"Oh, you know what I mean. He was a hoot, though, wasn't he? A jolly good mixer, as my aunt Bet used to say." Bella paused thoughtfully. "And of course you know it's a truth universally acknowledged that it isn't every man who can carry off the Hawaiian shirt/Hush Puppies combo."

"And what stories he had!" Molly added. "Imagine him being in that old black-and-white musical with Adam Faith. Amazing."

"Yes, and what about that hilarious one — the tale about meeting Prince Philip . . .?"

". . . and giving him advice on making the perfect cup of tea!"

It seemed that Ronald's life had been as colourful as his shirts and just as likely that his stories were more than a little embroidered, but that hardly mattered. He was such good fun.

"What did you make of Jack?" Bella asked. "A bit shy, don't you think? Still, I expect he's got hidden depths. You know, the strong, silent type like Clint Eastwood — only without the stubble and cigar."

Illustration by Mike Heslop.

by Victoria Greenhowe.

"Or the lovely poncho," Molly added. "Did he ever mention what he did before retiring? I don't think he said."

"Well, he wouldn't, would he, being all enigmatic and Clint Eastwood-like."

THERE had been six of them at the table each evening, the other couple being Steven and Wendy who were all for, as Steven enthused, "living life to the max". They were one of the younger couples, mid forties, most probably — "the teenagers", Bella called them, much to their delight. And that had been the set-up for twelve glorious, island-hopping

days sailing around Greece. Everybody got along fabulously and Ronald, being Ronald, made everything go with an extra zing. Only Jack seemed a little out of place on occasion. Still, it was tricky having to share the limelight with Ronald, who could probably put up a fair job of outshining the Blackpool illuminations!

Needless to say it wasn't too long before Bella was making mischief in her own inimitable way.

"Wow, two men on the dangle, just wait till Jenny hears all about her mum's admirers."

"Don't be daft, I'm way past all that. Honestly, Bella, you read far too many romance novels. People only meet on cruises in one of your love stories. Real life is never like that."

"Oh, I don't know," Bella replied. "And no matter what you say, I just know they're both quite keen. Ronald's definitely interested. I saw him giving you the old glad eye over the ocean buffet."

"Glad eye?" Molly questioned. "Goodness, Bella, I think I last heard that in 1958."

"Well, whatever it's called nowadays. All means the same thing."

Bella thoroughly enjoyed making up her Mills and Boon scenario, albeit with three pensioners as the protagonists.

Molly didn't mind. How could she? They had been friends for ever and lately, both being widows, had started enjoying life again — pictures, meals, holiday adventures, new challenges. Never a dull moment with Bella!

* * * *

And now this. A letter from Ronald. And just one week after they had said their final goodbyes at the dock. Naturally, in the taxi home, Bella decided it had been just like the big farewell scene from "Casablanca".

Ronald's letter was buzzing with all sorts and everything, just like the man himself. He told an amusingly convoluted story about his journey home in the taxi, how he was doing in the bowls tournament (very well!), that his son was

Sisters

**SISTERS they are, yet some are tall
And splendid, others very small,
So tiny, delicate and fair,
One has to search to find them there.**

**While some are cared for tenderly,
Others will flourish wild and free,
Each beautiful in her own right,
Moonbeam-pale, or sunset-bright.**

**Some heads are raised and some are bowed,
Some shy, some justifiably proud,
As, gloriously arrayed, they vie,
To touch the heart and thrill the eye.**

**Synonymous with joy, and yet,
A fount of comfort when we fret,
Their gentle beauty helps us heal
Any sorrow we may feel.**

**As seasons come and seasons go,
Small wonder that we love them so . . .
How they enhance this world of ours,
Sweet, starry sisterhood of flowers!**

— Kathleen O'Farrell.

"going up" in the world of stairlifts and that he himself was busy signing up a new "lady friend" for computer classes at the library.

Somehow, Molly wasn't too surprised he asked few questions about how she was doing. Nor did he mention "meeting up some time" as he often had on the cruise. Now she really considered it, Ronald wasn't one to ask questions. To be honest, he wasn't much of a listener, either. Not like Jack.

More and more lately, Molly had been remembering Jack and their special times together, just the two of them. Returning from an onshore excursion — Jack helping carry her bag full of goodies from an enthusiastic shopping trip. He had listened as she'd rambled on about life at home, her love of chocolate, her fear of spiders — oh, all sorts of silly nonsense. And best of all, he made her laugh. In truth, she hadn't felt such warmth and companionship since her long and happy marriage to David. And if she were honest, it had scared her just a little. She wasn't sure she wanted to feel that way again.

NATURALLY, Molly mentioned Ronald's letter when they met up at the cinema.

"See, it's all happening!" Bella enthused, ordering a giant tub of popcorn. "This could be the start of a beautiful friendship. What's it to be, salty or sweet?"

"Sweet," Molly replied, saying nothing further of her vague disappointment in Ronald's letter and her even deeper disappointment in not hearing from Jack.

The holiday photos were the usual odd assortment. Funny, but Molly always half-hoped she'd come across as a combination of Sophia Loren and Judi Dench and was always somewhat surprised by the "old lady" smiling back at her.

But there they all were — the gang — outside that cheerful little street café with the exuberant owner who sang all his orders; Steven in a silly hat, giving Wendy a big kiss; Bella on the dance floor, dancing the samba with Jonathan, the young and impossibly handsome steward. It was good to see them all together again, just as she remembered them. Except . . . Molly lingered over the photograph of the two of them posing with the captain. He was taller than she remembered.

Not the captain. Jack. Lovely, smiling Jack.

THE cruise became a memory, with Molly tucking the photos away in her album, except for one which she pinned under the fridge magnet.

"What's this?" Bella asked, nodding towards it.

"I think it's a good one of me," Molly tried to explain, none too convincingly.

"Nothing to do with Jack, then. Look, he's got his arm around your waist."

"He has not!" Molly protested.

"Well, he's thinking about it, you can tell." She paused, a sparkle in her eye. "You liked him, didn't you?"

"There wasn't anything not to like," Molly agreed, feeling like a teenager feigning indifference for the hunky head prefect.

"And you haven't heard from him at all," Bella mused, puzzled. "Well, why don't you write? You should, you know. Nothing ventured, and all that."

* * * *

Molly signed off her postcard to her best friend in all the world, unrepentant romantic, dedicated matchmaker and not so long ago a fabulous maid of honour.

A million thanks again, Bella, for the good advice. See you soon. Love always, Mrs Jack Roberts.

"Ready, then?" Jack asked Molly as they collected their backpacks.

"Ready! Where to?"

Jack smiled, kissed her with gusto and took her hand warmly in his own.

"Wherever the road leads us . . ."

Bella thought it just the most sublime Hollywood ending imaginable. Her best friend and her lovely new husband, honeymooning around Europe — in tents! Molly had thought it reckless, mad and, yes, wonderful, too.

"You're learning, kid." Bella had winked. "What are you waiting for — go for it! Live life!"

So Molly did just that — to the max! ■

A Father's Joy

by Kate Jackson.

ARE you sure, Dan?" my wife, Sophie, asks.

"Of course. We'll have a lovely time together, won't we, Millie?" I say to the cute bundle of joy I'm holding in my arms.

"Thanks." Sophie touches my arm. "It wasn't how I'd planned we'd spend your first Father's Day, but I can't leave Mum to struggle on her own."

"I know. It's fine. Honestly. Off you go and we'll see you later."

Sophie smiles and kisses us both.

"Oh, and don't forget Millie's afternoon nap in about an hour, otherwise she'll be tired and grumpy later," she calls back over her shoulder as she freewheels down the drive on her bicycle. "Bye, bye, then. See you later."

Millie and I stand on the doorstep and wave as Sophie pedals off in the direction of her parents' house.

"Mummy's gone to help your granny Judy," I say to Millie. "Because she can't manage on her own with her poor arm."

Sophie's mother broke her arm two weeks ago and needs some help today. Father's Day is an important one in Sophie's family. They always have a special meal in the late afternoon and Sophie's gone to help cook it. Millie and I will go along later. Each generation of fathers in Sophie's family will be there. Both of her grandfathers, her dad and, this year, for the first time, I'll be there as a father, too, adding another generation of fathers to the family tree.

"So, it's just you and me for the afternoon, Millie," I say, looking down at my gorgeous ten-month-old daughter.

She looks up at me with her big blue eyes and pulls a wide, gummy smile that just makes me melt inside like gooey toffee. Spending the afternoon here with Millie feels like the perfect thing to do on Father's Day. I've not

Illustration by Mark Viney.

had the chance to spend as much time as I'd like with her lately. For the past couple of months I've had to work away a lot and I've only seen her at weekends. It's a wonder she still recognises me.

Millie pats at my face with a chubby hand and smiles again.

"Come on, then, let's go and play."

FIVE minutes later we're both sitting on the rug in the front room and Millie's gradually emptying out the contents of the big wicker picnic chest where we keep her toys. I love the way she takes her time choosing, seriously considering what to pick out next. In the end she settles for some of the soft, brightly coloured material cubes. They've got the letters of the alphabet on each cube face with a picture representing the letter. Things like an apple for A, a ball for B and a wonderful bony X-ray for X. The cubes look so big in Millie's hands that she can only pick up one at a time.

"Can I help?" I ask. She looks at me and passes me the cube in her hands. "Shall I build you a tower?"

Together we pick the other five cubes out of the basket and I carefully pile them up, one on top of the other, to make a tower higher than Millie.

"There. What do you think of that?"

Millie crawls forward and reaches out with one hand. Her touch brings the whole tower tumbling down and she starts to laugh, looking at me, her eyes shining with delight.

"Again?" I ask, knowing full well that's what she'd like.

This tower toppling game is a favourite of hers. So I keep on building while she waits patiently and then knocks the tower down again. I try different variations: a pyramid, then two shorter towers side by side, but each one gets toppled down with a delightful giggle.

Millie would carry on knocking down my towers all day, but after a while I decide we need to do something else to help tire her out so she'll be ready for her nap.

"Come on, Millie," I say, getting down on my hands and knees. "Follow me."

Off I go, crawling to the door. I pause, looking back, and she's sitting there staring at me. I supposed she's not used to seeing me down here; usually she's looking up at me.

"Come on." I beckon her over. "This way."

She smiles and then quickly crawls over to me and we set off on a tour of the bottom floor of our house. Being down here gives me a different view of the place and makes me realise how high up some things are — like the kitchen benches and table. All out of reach, but so tempting for a curious child. Crawling around is hard on my knees. Millie doesn't seem to have a problem with hers, though, and I'm amazed at how quickly she can crawl.

We find our way back to the front room and end up having a hilarious game

Otter

RARELY spotted, though fondly thought of, thanks in part to the 1978 film "Tarka The Otter" and Gavin Maxwell's book "Ring Of Bright Water", otters are making something of a comeback since high levels of water pollution caused their numbers to drop dramatically during the 1960s.

In North Wales, in particular, evidence of otters can now be found in around seven out of ten riverbanks and wetland sites, and their numbers are healthy in northern and western Scotland.

Living near to the water in dens called holts or couches, otters feed mainly on fish and shellfish. They have very high metabolic rates to allow them to keep warm despite spending long periods in cold water — they need to eat around 15% of their bodyweight every day, which means hunting daily for up to five hours.

Also designed to enable otters to keep warm and dry is their fur, made up of a very soft, insulated under-fur, protected by an outer layer of long guard hair. Having two layers means that air is trapped in between.

The otter is part of the mustelid family, which also includes animals like weasels and stoats, and has the basic mustelid shape of a long, slim body. The otter, though, has adapted to life in the water with webbed feet for better swimming power, and has a strong tail that it uses to propel and steer itself.

Wildstock.

crawling round and round the sofa. Sometimes she goes one way and I go the other, waiting just around a corner, ready to pop out with a "boo" when she gets near. It makes us both giggle.

When my knees start to complain it's time to end the game.

"My knees are hurting," I say as I lift Millie up into my arms and hug her.

She cuddles into my chest and rubs her eyes, which is a sure sign she's getting tired.

"Let's have a story," I say, thinking a quiet read will help her relax.

I pick out one of her favourite picture books and we settle down in the corner of the sofa. Millie's snuggled up in the crook of my arm and she leans her head against me, looking at the colourful pictures in the book as I read the story. I've read it so many times before that I almost know it by heart.

I can feel her relaxing against me, but she's not asleep yet. Closing the book at the end of the story, I gently stand up and carry her upstairs to her room.

"It's time to sleep," I say softly, as I lay her down in her cot and pull the cover over her. I kiss her and then slide up the side of the cot so she's safe.

Tiptoeing out of the room, I half close the door and make my way downstairs. I'll use the time while she's asleep to get on with some work. Millie usually sleeps for about an hour and a half, so that will give me enough time to go through my notes before my meeting on Monday morning.

I've just switched on my laptop and got the papers out on my desk when there's a mighty yell from upstairs and Millie's crying fit to burst. Is she hurt? My heart's thudding as I run up the stairs to see what's wrong.

Rushing into her room, I find her standing up at the bars of her cot, red in the face from crying.

"Hey, sweetheart, what's wrong?" I pick her up and cuddle her to me.

She gradually calms down and her crying hiccups to a stop. I check her over and she looks fine. She even gives me a big gummy smile. There doesn't seem to be anything wrong with her. Maybe it was the cot. I shake off the cover to make sure there's nothing in there which might hurt her. Again, everything's fine.

"Come on, then, it's time to sleep, little one, or you'll be too tired later." I gently lay her down in the cot again, pull up the covers and kiss her cheek. "Sleep tight."

But I only get to the bottom of the stairs before she starts crying again. She doesn't usually do this when Sophie puts her down for a nap. There must be something wrong.

I SHOOT back up the stairs and pick up the sobbing Millie again. Just as she did before, she soon calms down and rubs her eyes with tiredness.

"I know you're tired, Millie. You need to get some sleep," I say. "I'm not far away — just downstairs."

So I put her down in her cot again, pull up the covers, kiss her, raise the side of the cot and leave. This time, I only get as far as the landing when she starts crying. I know she's all right, not hurt or anything. Maybe I should just leave her for a few minutes and she'll calm down.

So I go downstairs and sit down at my desk and try to work. But I can't. The noise of her crying pulls at something in me; it's like a thread tugging at my heart. I hate hearing my daughter so upset. There's nothing for it but to go back upstairs.

"Hush, Millie. It's OK," I tell her.

As soon as I pick her up she starts to calm down again and is soon smiling and cuddling into my chest. I know she's tired and needs to sleep, but she just won't settle down. And if she doesn't have a sleep she'll be tired and grumpy at the meal later on — and I won't get my work done, either.

So what do I do? My first thought is to ring Sophie, but I can't. I'd told her we'd be fine and I'd felt so confident that I could look after Millie on my own for a few hours. I've done it before. Looking after children isn't rocket science so I should be able to manage perfectly well without calling my wife for help when things don't go the way they should. Other men look after their children on their own all the time. I should be able to do it, too.

SUDDENLY I know what to do! I'll ring my friend, John, for some advice. He's got four children and he'll know how to deal with something like this.

Downstairs, with Millie still in my arms, I dial John's number and quickly explain the problem to him when he answers.

"You need to get her to sleep first and then put her down. Walk around with her resting on your shoulder; that's what I used to do," John says. "I nearly wore a track in the carpet with our eldest."

"Thanks, John. I'm not used to this."

"No problem. They don't come with an instruction manual." He laughs. "I'd just about got the hang of it by number four!"

I do as John suggested and walk around holding Millie against my chest with her head resting on my shoulder. As I circuit the front room for the tenth time I can feel her growing heavier and heavier as she drops off. A couple more laps and I am certain she's fast asleep.

I climb the stairs as smoothly as I can and lay her down in her cot just as I did before, only this time it looks like she's finally going to have her nap. I gently kiss her and tiptoe out of the room and down the stairs.

So far, so good. I've just settled down at my desk, opened up the file I need to work on and a loud cry starts up. Millie's awake again and giving her lungs a thorough workout. Back up the stairs I go again. This time, when I go in her room she's standing at the cot side with her arms held out to me, and tears running down her cheeks. My heart melts and I scoop her up and hug her.

"You're supposed to be asleep, little one," I say, kissing the top of her head.

"So much for John's idea. What am I going to do with you? You don't do this when Mummy puts you down for your nap."

Time's getting on and I have to do something. Maybe I should get a mother's advice. I can't ring Sophie, so I decide to ring my older sister, Jo. She's got three children so she's bound to know what to do.

"Put her in the pushchair and take her for a walk," Jo says. "The movement and fresh air will soon have her nodding off. When she's asleep go home and get on with what you need to do."

"Should I put her in her cot?" I ask.

"No. Leave her in the pushchair. Adjust the seat so she's lying down and make sure she's not too hot and have her somewhere you can keep an eye on her. She'll be fine."

Five minutes later, I'm pushing Millie down the lane in her pushchair. She seems happy to be going out and, to begin with, shows no sign of falling asleep. So I keep on walking and walking and eventually the magic of fresh air and the gentle movement of the pushchair along the road soothes her to sleep. And I turn for home.

BACK at the house I park the pushchair in the hall right near my office doorway, make sure she's not too hot and then stand back to enjoy the peace. Millie looks like a little sleeping angel, her long eyelashes lying lightly on her smooth cheeks.

While Millie sleeps, I get on with my work. I want it finished by the time she wakes so I don't waste a moment of being with her. I'm almost done when the phone rings.

"Hello, Dan," Sophie says. "How are you getting on?"

"Fine," I say. "Millie's still asleep."

"Good. I'm sorry but I just realised I forgot to tell you to wind up the music box when you put her down and make sure you draw the curtains in her room. It helps her to settle. But you've coped fine. I'm glad."

"Well . . ." I begin. But I'm interrupted by Sophie.

"Oh! The oven timer's pinging. I'll have to go, Dan. See you later." And she rings off without giving me a chance to tell her the sorry tale of my many attempts to get our daughter to have her nap.

Life's Little Things

BE happy in life's little things,
They always mean so much,
The simple pleasures each day brings,
A smile, a hug, a touch.
An unexpected call or card,
The sunshine after rain,
A helping hand when times are hard,
A well-loved sweet refrain.

Be happy in the diamond days,
They help your hopes revive.
Forget the steep and stony ways,
And keep your dreams alive.
Rejoice in all the little things,
They warm the heart and mind,
The many blessings each day brings
Are there for us to find.

— Iris Hesselden.

Millie's stirring in the pushchair and I shut down my laptop and go and pick up my daughter, whose cheeks are a beautiful rosy-pink from sleep.

"Let's go and sit down for a bit," I say as I carry her through to the front room and settle down on the sofa with her snuggled against my chest while she slowly returns to wakefulness.

It's lovely holding her, this little person whom I'm responsible for. It feels wonderful and scary and amazing all at the same time. That's what being a father is about, enjoying the fun stuff and coping with the hard bits.

As Millie comes back to full wakefulness her attention is caught by my watch. She starts to run her fingers around the metal links of my watch strap. One shell-tipped finger glides over the smooth glass of the dial. She's absorbed in exploring it, watching the second hand tick round.

I love watching her discovering her world. It makes me stop and look at things afresh, seeing them from different angles, taking time to stop and stare. I know I haven't done enough of that with Millie lately because of my work. I didn't even know that she has her music box wound up and curtains drawn when she has a nap. They're little things, I know, but they're part of her life. And I'm missing them.

"Come on, Millie," I say. "I'd better get you changed into that dress Mummy left out for you to put on." She looks up at me and smiles her gummy smile. "When we get to your granny Judy's we can tell Mummy about this afternoon and that I didn't know how to get you to sleep. Do you think she'll laugh at me?"

I think Sophie might. But there's something else I'm going to tell her, too. I'm going to change the way I work. I'm not going to work far away from home any more. I want to come home each night. Be with my family in the morning and the evening, not just weekends. I want to be with my daughter every day, not just on Father's Day. I think Sophie and Millie will like that. I know I will. ■

Elvis And Me

by Jill Paterson.

Illustration by Jaia.

"YOU'RE no' goin' oot like that and whit's this nonsense on the TV?" My mum stared at my yellow miniskirt and let out a sigh.

"It's a miniskirt, Mum, and that 'nonsense' is the most wonderful man in the world — Elvis Presley."

Mum put her hands on her hips and squinted at our black and white television.

"And is there a reason that he's jumpin' aboot daft like that?"

I stifled a giggle and joined her to gaze at the television.

There was a clip of Elvis on the screen — he was dancing around a stage and swinging his microphone stand to either side of him. He looked absolutely gorgeous.

"Isn't he marvellous?" I beamed and clasped my hands together.

Hector, our West Highland white terrier, seemed to share the same sceptical glance as my mother.

"I'll tell you what isna' marvellous — that so-called skirt! It's too short."

My yellow miniskirt with giant lemon polka dots all over it had set me back nearly a week's wages, but I loved it.

"It's the fashion," I protested.

"So be it. You're an adult now!" She scowled and headed off for the kitchen. "Hector!" she called and our wee dog ran after her as he always did.

It was five o'clock and Linda would soon be here. I loved nothing more than going to the dance hall every Saturday night and doing the twist, the mashed potato and the funky chicken with my best friend. We had such a giggle!

I WENT along for the dancing and the Elvis records, but lately Linda had had an alternative reason. She had had her eye on Kenny Charlton for quite some time. Tall, clean-shaven and with his sandy hair swept into a side parting, Kenny always looked handsome.

He seemed to like chatting away to Linda every Saturday and he often asked her to dance, but he'd never actually asked her out. This baffled Linda and she had a million theories about why it had never happened.

"Maybe he's got another girl, maybe he's just had his heart broken or maybe he just doesn't like me," she said as she sat on my bed later that evening.

I backcombed a portion of my hair and it looked like a tuggy mess.

"I doubt that," I replied. "He always looks as though he can't wait to see you."

"You really think so?"

"Mmm-hmm," I said with a kirby grip between my teeth. I pulled a layer of hair back over the backcombing and my beehive was complete.

"What about you, Brenda, when are you going to agree to go out with a lad?"

I pondered Linda's question. I had no interest in a lad. I liked my life just fine, staying with Mum, working in the watch factory, listening and dreaming of Elvis every night and going dancing every weekend. I really had no time for an ordinary man.

"I don't know. Not just now anyway."

My dad had died from a heart attack when I was just four years old and it had been me and Mum ever since. We had only ever needed each other from then on. I suppose seeing her being so independent and strong had had an impact on me.

THAT night the dance hall was buzzing with full-of-fun twenty-somethings. There were lots of brightly coloured miniskirts on show and the boys all looked well-groomed with their jazzy shirts and neat cardigans.

After a few twists, we stopped for a drink of lemonade and it didn't take long before Kenny waved over to Linda then appeared at the counter beside us.

"Hi, ladies!" he greeted us.

"Hi, Kenny," we both replied. Linda batted her eyelashes while I frowned, knowing that I was about to be abandoned for a portion of the night. I was getting just the tiniest bit fed up with it.

Kenny asked Linda up for a jive and I stood alone and finished my lemonade.

"Cheer up, dollface. It could be worse," a familiar voice said.

I looked up to see Frank Malone leaning on the counter with a grin.

"Hi, Frank," I said with a light tone. I liked Frank, but I knew he wasn't for me. He was nice and funny and very confident, but there was something missing.

"Dance?"

"No, thanks," I replied gently.

He moved closer to me, his soft hair almost touching my face.

"You know, Brenda, one of these days you might just ask me to dance and I might say no."

I laughed. Every week Frank asked for a dance and every week I said no. I didn't want him to get the wrong impression and think that I might be interested in him.

"Keep on wishing, Frank."

"I will. You're just like a big block of ice."

"I am?"

"Yes, and if I just keep chipping away, you'll crack."

"Aren't you a charmer?" I joked.

His grin grew wider and he looked at Linda and Kenny on the dance floor.

"Look at how much fun they're having. That could be us."

"Yeah, they're having fun now, but she'll be all teary-eyed when the lights come up and he still hasn't asked her out."

"What would be the point in him doing that?" he asked, genuinely puzzled.

"So she could be his girl," I replied as though he needed his head checked.

"How could she be his girl when he'll be in Australia?"

I paused.

"Australia?"

"He's going to live with his aunt and uncle in Sydney."

"When?" I demanded.

"Next week, I think."

I put my glass of lemonade down on the counter and turned to him seriously.

"Wait a minute, how do you know this?"

"His chum, Keith Black, is also a friend of mine."

"Oh." My heart sank for Linda. "Why hasn't he told her?"

Frank shrugged.

"Maybe he thought she wouldn't want to spend time with him any more if she knew he was going away."

"Too right she wouldn't! She could be finding herself someone else."

Frank turned his head to the side and looked me up and down.

"But what if he's the one for her?"

I scoffed.

"Nonsense! There's no such thing."

He shook his head and laughed slightly.

"Well, Brenda, all I can say is that you don't have a romantic bone in your body." He grinned and casually went on his way.

Was he right? Was I completely unromantic? I decided that I wasn't at all — if Elvis asked me out, I'd say yes in a heartbeat. But no man that I knew could measure up to my idol. That wasn't unromantic, that was simply realistic.

ON the way home, I wondered how on earth I was going to tell Linda about Kenny. She had been unusually quiet and the only sound was our high heels clicking on the cobbles.

"Linda," I began.

"Yes?" She looked up at me with watery eyes.

"I don't quite know how to say this, but . . . well, Kenny's going to live in Australia."

She didn't answer for a moment.

"I know," she said finally.

"You know?"

"He told me tonight."

"Oh, Linda, I'm sorry, I know how much you liked him."

"It's OK. I'll miss him, but I can wait for him."

I stopped walking in surprise while Linda strolled on ahead.

"Why on earth would you do that?"

"Because I love him," she replied as she stopped and turned round.

I caught up with her and put my arm around her.

"But he might not come back and you could get hurt," I protested, willing her to see sense.

"I won't get hurt. He loves me, too, and he's only going for a year."

"Don't be so naïve," I told her.

She threw my arm off her shoulders.

"You are entitled to your own opinion, Brenda, and so am I! I believe that he loves me and he will come back for me."

"Then you're a daft wee lassie, as my mum would say." I never thought I would be quoting my mother quite yet, but it slipped out before I had thought it through.

"And you're an awful friend!" With that, she was off and running up the cobbles.

A few drops of rain touched my face and I looked up at the murky sky. I hadn't meant to upset Linda — I thought I was just looking out for her. I was more like my mother than I had realised.

BY the time I got home, I looked like I had been thrown into the river. My beehive was as flat as pancake, my layers of mascara were running down my face and my miniskirt looked more like a dishcloth than designer fabric.

Mum approached the door as I came in.

"Look at the state of you, missus!" she bellowed as Hector came to her side. "Let me get you a towel."

She returned seconds later with a big, white fluffy towel and wrapped it around my shoulders.

"Get into your nightie and I'll put the kettle on."

I did as I was told and ten minutes later I was on the settee, cosy and comfortable, sharing a cup of tea with my mum.

Usually I would just fall into my bed after a night of dancing, but Mum could tell there was something up.

"Right. Whit's happened the night?" she asked.

"Nothing," I replied.

"Then why does your face look like it's been skelped?"

I sighed.

"I had a fight with Linda. She was being daft about a boy."

"And I suppose you telt her so?" she asked, raising an eyebrow.

Enniskillen Castle

ENNISKILLEN CASTLE'S location is no accident — it commands an important strategic crossing of the River Erne between the Upper and Lower lakes. While it may look like an odd selection of buildings, this reflects this Irish castle's history — built in the early fifteenth century by Hugh "the Hospitable" Maguire, it was rebuilt by Captain William Cole in the early 1600s, nearly ruined by fire in 1710, then refurbished as a military barracks in the late eighteenth century, as which it served until 1926.

Visitors today can enjoy the Fermanagh County Museum, reflecting the area's rich history, culture and environment.

I nodded.
"Linda can make her own decisions."
"But this boy is going to Australia and she's going to wait for him."
"Well, that's her choice."
"But —"
"Your granny thought I was silly to wait for your dad."
I gave her a puzzled look.
"We had known each other since we were wee, but we were jist good pals. Then, right before he was called up for service, he asked me to marry him."
"Without even courting you first?" I asked in amazement.
"According to him, he'd been courting me his whole life!"
"Did you say yes right then?"
"No. I had never thought of him like that before. I said I needed time to think aboot it. But while he was away, I missed him so much. He was my other half — he always had been."
"So you waited for him?"
"Yes. And he came back, we got married and had you."
She gave my hand a squeeze.
"Linda's not talking to me now," I announced.
"She will soon enough. Just give her time to calm doon."

BUT Linda didn't calm down and I didn't get the chance to apologise. I called round, but she wasn't home. She always came up to mine on Saturday night, but by seven o'clock, I realised that she wasn't coming and there would be no twisting that night.

So, I sat alone in my bedroom with Hector on my knee and listened to Elvis records over and over again. After the fifth play of "Jailhouse Rock" Mum poked her head round the door and begged me to play a different song.

As I put on "Heartbreak Hotel" I started thinking about where my infatuation with Elvis had come from.

It had started a few years back when I'd seen him on TV for the first time. And since then, I'd had no thoughts of having a boyfriend, even though all of my friends seemed to be swooning over someone.

It occurred to me that maybe I was using Elvis as a distraction so I didn't have to think about boys. At that moment, I remembered what Mum had said about Dad being the other half of her all that time and I realised that I was not only missing Linda and the dance hall, but I was also missing Frank.

I had got so used to chatting to him, seeing his friendly grin and piercing green eyes. But I had refused a dance with him so many times that it was nothing more than a running joke now. I had been afraid of letting him into my life. I had been afraid of romance.

I rushed through to the kitchen, where Mum was putting some food into Hector's bowl.

"Mum! Where's my dress with all the orange squares on it?"
"In the ironing," she answered.
"Could you press it for me while I do my hair, please?"
She looked at the cuckoo clock on the wall.
"But it's half-past nine. Where are you going at this time?"
"To the dance hall."
"On your own?"
"Yes, but there's a lad that I want to ask to dance."
"You shouldn't be asking him —"
"Oh, Mum, that doesn't matter! I have to see him."
I could tell that she had never seen me so emotional over a boy.
"Right, I'll press it, and you do whatever that nonsense is that makes your hair stand six feet in the air."
I kissed her cheek and hurried into my bedroom.

BY the time I got to the dance hall, there was only half an hour of dancing left. I spotted Frank right away, but my heart started beating faster as I noticed that he was talking to a gorgeous blonde wearing a cute Alice band with a pink frilly blouse and a swirly white skirt.
I had missed the boat. Frank had found another girl that he wanted to dance with and she probably wasn't silly enough to turn him down.
As I turned to leave the hall, Linda appeared in front of me.
"Linda!"
"Hi, Brenda," she said. "I'm sorry I didn't come up to yours tonight, but Kenny leaves tomorrow and we wanted to come to the dance hall together."
"I understand." I paused, trying to figure out what to say next. "I'm sorry about what I said. I didn't mean it."
She smiled a little and took my hand.
"I know I'm taking a chance on Kenny, but I suppose time will tell."
I gave her hand a squeeze.
"Some chances are worth taking," I told her.
Just then, I felt a hand on my shoulder and turned to see Frank and the blonde by my side.
"Hi, Frank!" I beamed, pretending not to be bothered by the beauty at his side.
"Brenda, I'd like you to meet my little sister, Joyce."
Joyce extended her hand and grinned, the same friendly smile as Frank.
"Oh . . . I thought . . ." I stammered and Linda gave me a glance that indicated I hadn't shaken Joyce's hand, but had left it rudely floating in mid-air.
"Hello, Joyce. It's nice to meet you," I said and grasped her hand.
"So you're the girl who won't dance with my brother," she commented, still smiling.

I blushed.

"That's me!" I laughed nervously.

"Is this your first time here, Joyce?" Linda asked.

"It is. And I can't get a minute's peace for Frank following me around like a bodyguard."

Linda laughed.

"Fancy a lemonade?" She linked her arm through Joyce's and off they went to the counter.

There was an awkward silence and Frank put his hands in his pockets.

"I saw Linda and Kenny earlier, but there was no sign of you," he said.

"I only decided at the last minute to come along." I took a deep breath. "So I could ask you to dance."

He looked shocked.

"And so you could say no and then we would be even."

"It would take a lot more than one 'no' for us to be even," he joked.

"Fair enough," I said lightly, pretending to stare at my nails. "I'll just come back every week and ask you until we're even."

He laughed.

"What changed your mind?"

"Elvis," I replied. "I got thinking about him then you. I missed you."

He grinned.

"Well, seeing as Elvis brought us together, do you fancy going to see 'Girl Happy' on Wednesday night?"

I considered it for a second.

"Could we see 'Dr Zhivago' instead? I think I've had enough of Elvis for just now."

"Whatever you like. Would you like to dance to the last song?" he asked and reached for my hand.

"I'd love to."

A **YEAR** later, Frank and I got married and bought a little flat two streets away from Mum. She said Hector was getting my room and hoped that now I was a married woman I would wear more sensible clothes.

The day we got the keys to our flat, we danced around the red carpet in our living-room to Manfred Mann. Kenny and Linda were coming round later to help us celebrate, although there wasn't a chair for them to sit on.

Kenny, true to his word, had returned from Australia a year later and proposed to Linda.

I took Frank in my arms and kissed him.

"That was very romantic," he said with a smile.

"See," I replied. "I do have at least one romantic bone in my body."

He just laughed and kissed me again. ■

Hare

THE European hare or brown hare is native to western Europe and the UK. It is related to the rabbit, but does not breed in a burrow and relies on speed to escape from predators. Powerful hind legs mean that hares have been known to reach speeds of 45 mph!

The hare is larger, longer-eared and longer-legged than a rabbit. A herbivore, it eats grasses and herbs during the summer months, but changes its diet to include twigs, bark and young trees in winter.

The hare's normally shy behaviour changes dramatically in spring when hares can be seen "boxing" in broad daylight. This was thought at one time to be a competition between males to gain more breeding partners, but is now thought to be females hitting males to prevent this happening. Now you'll understand the origin of the well-known phrase "mad as a March hare"!

The main difference between a hare and a rabbit is their habitat. Rabbits live underground in burrows or warrens, but hares live in nests above the ground. They do not, like rabbits, live in groups, either.

The hare is often seen as having mystical powers in Irish folklore. Anyone who dares to harm a hare in these stories always ends up coming to no good.

Wildstock.

On Appleton Thorn . . . by Pamela Kavanagh.

NOBODY rightly knew the origins of bawming the thorn. Old Jim Madeley, who couldn't remember the year of his birth but must be eighty if he was a day, said they'd been bawming the thorn here at Appleton ever since Adam were a lad. And who were we to argue?

For us children, the raggedy old hawthorn tree on the green with its massed pink blossom — pink, not common hedgerow white — held a magic that never failed to enchant. Midsummer wouldn't have been the same without the annual ritual of adorning the tree with ribbons and garlands.

After the ceremony we'd hold hands and dance round the tree, chanting the age-old rhyme that all Appleton folks were born knowing.

"Up with fresh garlands this midsummer morn.

Up with fresh ribbons on Appleton Thorn."

Following the bawming ceremony the village wives would put on a feast, and after that the fun would commence. There were tumblers and mummers. We'd run races and the older boys would have a tug-of-war.

Best of all was the fancy-dress parade. Every year we'd try to outdo each other in what we represented. Nursery rhyme characters were the usual choice, or countryside themes, flower-sellers or scarecrows, depending on one's gender.

But children grow up, and on the year I was fifteen and Thomas Halliwell seventeen, unbeknown to one another and quite without guile, we both went for a more adult form of dress.

I went as a corn-maiden and Thomas, tall, laughing, brown-haired Thomas, came as the green man. Nobody thought anything of it. As I said, we were innocent, and still children in the eyes of the village.

It all might have passed off innocuously as a little harmless fun had it not been for Maisie Dodd. For Maisie also turned up as a corn-maiden, and Maisie was no child.

Where my dress was nothing more than a rustic smock made over from a faded cotton bedspread, hers was a gown that clung daringly to her well-developed curves. And where I wore on my rioting chestnut mop a simple chaplet of daisies, her blonde ringlets sported a come-hither assortment of wayside blooms.

The looks of disapproval were rife and Mistress Gibbs pronounced loudly that it was high time the Dodd girl stood down, even though she was much

Illustration by Andre Leonard.

the same age as myself. Worst of all for me, Thomas, being male and impressionable, was instantly smitten.

I liked Thomas, of course I did. His mam and mine had been bridesmaids at each other's weddings. As village wise-woman, my mam had delivered Thomas and his siblings. Thomas was the big brother I'd never had. But there comes a time when sisterly feelings mature and become something else — an emotion I sensed rather than knew, and could not begin to understand.

What I did know was that seeing Maisie making sheep's eyes at Thomas on that sun-drenched June day made me want to scratch those big blue eyes out of her smug pink-and-white face!

Later, I felt a tug on my sleeve and there was our Violet, giggling because she'd seen Thomas kissing Maisie by the stile to Farmer Halliwell's meadow.

To top it all, before the day was over, Maisie came sauntering up with that hip-swaying walk of hers.

"Hello, Rosie. You and my Thomas have been friends a long time."

Her Thomas? I felt my hackles rise.

"Just like brother and sister, ain't you?" she continued, smiling that mischievous smile. "It won't come to anything. It's me as Thomas likes — but then don't they all!"

"See if I care!" I said, chin high.

But I did care. I cared very much indeed. It was an end to childhood and all things sweet and good. So wounded was I that, when night fell, I sneaked back to the green and snatched Maisie's garland down from the tree and hurled it into the river.

Triumphant, I stood on the bridge and watched the current carry it away. Soon there was nothing to be seen in the inky surface but the bobbing sliver of a new moon.

Glancing up at that slender arc high above, I swallowed. Mam said that an act made during a new moon always had repercussions. Had I ill-wished Maisie? I hadn't meant to. It wasn't Maisie I wanted rid of, but her offering to the hawthorn. For that, it struck me with a force that made me gasp, was what bawming the thorn was all about. We were giving our blessing and asking the tree for protection throughout the year to come. Would the tree now withdraw its goodwill?

"Mam," I said next morning. "If you do something you shouldn't, how do you take it back?"

We were in the stillroom tacked on to the back of the cottage, where the simples and salves were made. Mam looked up from her pounding.

"Why, Rosie Tucker . . ." she began.

All three of us were named for the flowers. I was Rose, then came Violet and lastly baby Marigold.

"You make recompense, of course," she continued. "Understand?"

"Yes." My heart sank. "It means give back what you value most."

“That’s my clever girl.”

Mam picked up the pestle and went back to mashing her herbs. How would I go about making amends?

The answer was all too obvious. I’d have to forego my friendship with Thomas. What did it matter, anyway, considering he preferred Maisie to me?

NEXT morning, on my way to the big house where I worked in the sewing-room, Thomas came rattling up behind me with the horse and cart.

“How do, Rosie.” He pulled up. “I’m going to the mill. Want a lift?”

“No, thank you. I’m happy walking.” I stiffened my resolve.

Thomas frowned.

“It’s a fair trek and it’s on my way.”

“Thanks, but I can take a short cut across the fields.”

Thomas knew how I hated getting my shoes and hems wet with dew and his frown deepened in puzzlement.

“Anyway,” I said, “you might come across Maisie on the road. You can give her a lift.”

Thomas shrugged.

“Right-oh, have it your own way.”

He sent the horse away at a spanking trot, stirring clouds of dust that got up my nose and made me cough and splutter. Serve me right, I thought, seeing in my mind’s eye that garland being whisked off by the river.

The day went from bad to worse. I was embroidering a petticoat of finest lawn for her ladyship when my usually deft needle slipped, spotting the fabric with blood. Mistress Tewke, who was in charge of us, uttered a sharp rebuke.

“Careless girl! Go and wash it out. Cold water, mind, and be quick about it before it stains. Mind you bind the finger up. And watch what you’re about in future, or it’ll be back to the everyday mending with you! Mind me, Rose?”

“Yes’m.”

Mortification flooding my cheeks, I left the room and was aware of the sniggers of glee from the other girls as I shut the door.

The bandaged finger made me clumsy and I had to unpick the morning’s work and start again. Nor was I allowed to leave until the task was done to my mistress’s satisfaction, and shadows were long-drawn across the fields as I trudged home.

Several days passed before I saw Thomas again. He’d obviously waylaid Maisie on her way back from dairy-maiding at the farm, for they stood at the gates, talking together.

“Hey, Rosie,” he called to me. “Come and join us.”

I wanted to, but my resolve strengthened.

"No, thank you," I said and, ignoring his bemusement, I quickened my stride and went on by.

At home, Mam was in a flap because Marigold had toddled into the stillroom and mixed up the rubbed herbs Mam had left on the bench.

"Bad girl! All that work wasted."

"Oh, Mam, she didn't mean it." The sight of my little sister's woebegone face was too much. I scooped her into my arms and hugged her. "There, then. We'll have to get Father to make a catch on the door."

Mam sniffed.

"Pigs might fly! I've been requesting that for weeks, but does he listen? Not a bit of it."

"I'll do it, if you like," I said.

It was only a matter of hammering a small piece of wood on the door that would swivel and hold it snug, but this not being my lucky day, the hammer slipped and came down on my thumb. It was all I needed.

Mam produced her healing salve and happily, by morning, my injuries were on the way to being cured.

"You're growing up fast," Mam said, back to her smiling self as she dished out the porridge. "It's high time I taught you my craft. You'll make a good wise-woman."

Me? Rosie Tucker, who'd tempted the wrath of the Thorn? Mam would throw up her hands in horror if she knew the half of it.

I mumbled I was happy as I was and left it at that.

In truth, I liked my job well enough. Fine stitching came easily to me and I loved the coloured silks and precious fabrics that abounded at the manor. That said, the thought of following in my mother's footsteps enticed. A village wise-woman had status and earned respect, as well as the payment that came in kind if the sufferer was short of ready coin. A pitcher of goats' milk, a hatful of eggs. It was payment enough when times were hard. But was I worthy of the position? I didn't think so.

W**EEKS** passed, and with Maisie Dodd looking as blooming as ever, I grew complacent. No going down with a mysterious fever, or coming out in boils that would ruin her complexion. Either my sacrifice was working or I had overreacted. Nothing would come of my shameful fit of midsummer pique.

September came. On the harvest fields the women worked alongside the men, gathering the cut corn and binding it into stooks. Everyone lent a hand at corn harvest and when my day's work at the big house was done I'd go and join them.

Thomas was there, working tirelessly. Maisie was there, too, bringing baskets of food. There was cider for the menfolk and, for the women, buttermilk cold from the dairy.

Tripping lightly over the shorn ground she came, cool and trim where we were hot and sun-baked, corn bits prickling our skin and bodices damp with sweat. A blue kerchief sat over her yellow curls and the whiteness of her apron dazzled the eye.

The men were appreciative, poor fools.

"Here's a pretty maid!"

"Bonnie as they come."

"Going to give us a kiss, then?"

She shook her head, blushing, and doled out the food. It was easy to guess who Maisie saved her kisses for and a great sadness took me. Thomas — my friend no more. We hardly ever spoke now. What was the point? And, anyway, there was my recompense to consider.

And then Maisie, making sheep's eyes at the menfolk over her shoulder, tripped and fell on the rutted ground and skinned her palms. Her wails sent half the village running to her side, Thomas amongst them, of course. Mam was there with her simples bag and I was back to castigating myself for my wickedness.

What next? Were the autumn sniffles that went around the village my fault, too? Mam had a decoction ready and waiting, a nose-tickling mix that soon sorted the problem. But yet I worried still, and worry stripped the flesh from my bones and robbed my cheeks of colour. I'd tried to mend my

Magic Smiles

A SPECIAL time and magic place.
As the seaside fills with fun,
Beach huts with no vacancies
Show summer has begun.
They're painted in the sunny shades
Of lilac, pink and lime,
The artist's palette all a-glow
This happy summertime.
Lapping round the shoreline,
The sea shines green and rose,
And a warm, cream beach is welcoming
For tiny, lively toes.
Then all at once the thunder comes,
And growls across the sky,
Till darkened threat turns blue again,
And the magical sun shines high.

— Dorothy McGregor.

wicked ways and plainly it hadn't worked. What more could I do?

It all came to a head a couple of months later. November hung grey over the fields and woods. Daylight seemed to have deserted us; the lane on my daily trudge to and from the manor was all puddle and muck.

One evening I was heading home from work, stumbling a little in the darkness, my feet squelching in the quaggy ground, when a black shape loomed ahead. Alarm frittered through me, and then the unmistakable whiff of horse turned my fright to laughter. It was only Farmer Halliwell's draught mare, standing there fully harnessed and bewildered and effectively blocking the path.

"Hello, girl," I said, stroking her bony nose. "What are you doing here all on your own?"

"Rosie? Is that you?"

I jumped, starting back in fright. But the voice was all too familiar and I soon recovered my senses.

"Thomas?" Worriedly I peered this way and that into the gloom. "Thomas, where are you? What's wrong?"

"Here, on the bank. Thank goodness you've come. I was beginning to think I'd be here all night."

Feeling my way past the bulky form of the horse, I came across Thomas sitting in the sodden grass of the wayside. It was too dark to see properly, but judging by his gasping breath he was in some pain.

Forgetting my resolve, forgetting everything but the urgency of the moment, I dropped to my knees at his side.

"Thomas, what's wrong?"

"It's my foot. I can't seem to put any weight on it."

"Oh, Thomas! You're hurt! Oh, this is all my fault."

"Get away! It was Amber's doing. I was leading her back from the fields when we came to grief in the mud and she trod on my foot — the clumsy beast! I thought she'd go on to the farm and give the alarm. But it seems she chose to keep me company!" Thomas half smiled.

"Oh, Thomas. Your poor foot. Is it very bad?"

"Well, Amber's no featherweight," Thomas said ruefully. He shifted to a more comfortable position, wincing. "Ouch. Let's hope my boot will have taken the brunt of it. I was counting on you coming this way, Rosie. Could you could fetch help?"

"Of course I will . . ."

Mam came right away, while I hurried on to the farm to tell them what had happened. A stretcher was rigged from a hurdle and very soon Thomas was home, lying on the kitchen settle in front of a blazing fire, while Mam examined the rapidly purpling injury.

"Nothing broken," she said. "The bruising is coming out and that's all to the good. 'Tis nothing a comfrey poultice won't cure; but you'll not be working for a day or two, Thomas, my lad."

Mam looked from Thomas to me.

"Here's your chance to practise, Rosie. I'll show you what to do and you can drop in morning and night and see to it. He'd best have a dose of poppy juice, too, for the pain. All right, Thomas?"

"Sounds all right to me," Thomas said.

WITHIN the week Thomas was hobbling round on crutches his father concocted from a couple of broom staves. I was still calling, applying the comfrey, offering poppy juice and sympathy.

"You've got a fine touch, Rosie. I'll be back at work in no time."

Thomas was more like his old self now. He sent me a questioning look.

"What did you mean that night when you said it was your fault? What was your fault?" he asked me.

"Well . . . I . . . oh, it's like this."

Out it all came. The June bawming, Maisie Dodd and what I had done with her garland.

"Little fool!" He took my hand in his and pressed it tenderly, smiling at me all the while. "You don't want to believe all that nonsense."

"But Maisie tumbled and hurt herself. It was all my doing."

"Fiddle! She tripped and that's all there is to it. If she'd looked where she was going it would never have happened."

"Do you think so?" I said wistfully. Then I steeled myself. "You were kissing her by the stile. You can't deny it, Thomas. Our Violet saw you."

"Did she now?" The smile became a grin — that dear, lopsided grin I knew so well. "Strikes me as you were jealous after all, Rosie."

"Well, what do you think?" I said, blushing furiously.

"I think it was a ruse of mine that went sadly wrong. I thought if I made a pass at Maisie it might make you look more kindly on me. A bit of healthy rivalry, like. Stop you treating me like a brother and more like . . . well, a sweetheart."

"Are you saying it meant nothing, that kiss?" I hardly dared to hope.

"I know where my heart lies." Thomas took hold of my other hand so I was powerless to move. "Ah, Rosie. Don't look at me like that. Tell me you haven't given me up as a bad job."

"Never that, Thomas."

"That's my girl," Thomas said, and drawing me to him he smacked a kiss on my lips. There was nothing brotherly about that kiss and, bones melting, I returned it readily.

Everything was fine between us after that. All the same, just to be sure, I picked an offering of rowan sprigs, bright with berries, and left them at the foot of the hawthorn tree that was used for the bawming. Like Mam says, better safe than sorry. ■

Hearts And Flowers

by Elise Mayle.

MRS SNELL, the village dressmaker, was an old woman with arthritic fingers and a hump on her back. But she sewed like an angel — snowy, frothy, dream-like dresses for brides.

"Stop wriggling, child," she told Lucy. "I've made some bridesmaid dresses in my time, but I can't remember when I've had such problems. You're more like an eel than a child. Stand still!"

Lucy, who privately thought Mrs Snell was a witch, held her breath and went red in the face.

"I'm wriggling because you stuck a pin in me."

"That's because you won't stand still. Believe me, it's no pleasure fitting you." She pushed in her last pin then stood back to eye Lucy critically. "Yes, that will do. Take a look at yourself and tell me what you think."

Lucy gazed at herself in the long mirror in silence.

"Well?" the dressmaker demanded.

The image that looked back at Lucy was one so unfamiliar, so surprising, that she didn't know what to say. The young girl in the mirror looked taller, older than

Illustration by Tim Art-McLaughlin.

seven years, her skin rosily reflecting the pink of the dress.

"It's a beautiful dress, Mrs Snell."

"Well, you don't look bad, I must say," the old woman conceded.

Lucy continued to stare. The dress was long, the first long one she had had in her life. She pinched the skirt, smiling secretly to herself.

"Don't stand there gawping, child," Mrs Snell scolded. "Off with that dress and let me finish it. The wedding's only two weeks away and I've still a stitch or two to put to your sister's dress."

Two weeks to go — Lucy couldn't believe it! At first it had seemed like a dream, listening to her mother and Maggie talking about "the wedding".

"Early summer, don't you think?" Her older sister's eyes shone as she sat at the breakfast table, waving a piece of toast in the air.

Lucy who, a moment ago, had watched her mother laugh with delight and fling her arms round her daughter, felt proud that she had been the first to know Maggie was going to marry Mike.

"And I don't want a string of bridesmaids . . . just Lucy."

The women's gaze turned to her.

"What colour do you think? Apricot would be nice, or blue."

"Pink." Maggie was adamant. "It's Lucy's colour. Something simple, sleeveless, I think. Yes, pink, with little roses in her hair."

"June," her mother mused. "I hope it will be a good summer."

IT was. It began to arrive with blue skies and a shiny sun — fresh, bright mornings drawing Lucy closer to the moment when she would be bridesmaid for the first time in her life.

Pink, Maggie had said and pink it was, gradually coming to life from the day they had gone to choose the material. There had been the moment when the shop assistant brought down rolls of rose silk and the bright pink taffeta, and another when she unrolled a sheath of white stuff that was soft and gauzy against her hand as she bunched it up for Maggie to see.

"How about this for the veil?"

All this was magic to Lucy: the veil, the special food that went with the wedding, the secret of Maggie's dress. Mike mustn't see it until "the day". Once, when they were at Mrs Snell's for a fitting, Mike had arrived unexpectedly and there had been a panic in case he got a glimpse.

As for Mike himself, Lucy wasn't sure what she thought of him. He was tall with a cheerful face, apt to corner her and demand answers to a lot of questions, using the hearty voice of someone who isn't used to talking to children.

Usually, when he came to the house, she rushed upstairs to the room she shared with Maggie and lay on her bed, reading. She loved to lie and read, and daydream.

She was shy, especially just now because she had to wear a brace on her teeth. Her mother hugged her and called her an ugly duckling, promising her that one day she would be a swan. But that wasn't now and she hated

Thinkstockphotos.

having to smile at people she didn't know very well. She dreaded the moment when Maggie called up the stairs.

"Lucy! Mike's here. Come and say hello to him."

They were sitting on the sofa holding hands and laughing together. This part of the wedding Lucy didn't understand, nor did she particularly want to. It was the dresses that interested her: Maggie's snowy-white dress and her own pretty pink one — the dresses and the cake with the tiny figures on the top layer.

She loved to lie awake, waiting for her sister to come to bed. The door would open and there was the sound of Maggie moving cautiously round the room until Lucy whispered, "Mags, I'm awake."

Then there was a delicious interlude of talking in whispers. She never tired of hearing more about this wedding — it had become like a bedtime story, her sister's soft voice coming through the darkness until Lucy's eyes wouldn't stay open any longer and she drifted off to sleep.

Lucy adored Maggie, who had always treated her like someone of her own age. She allowed her to play with her make-up and told her about the things she did and the people she met.

"Maggie," she began on the night of that last fitting when Mrs Snell had made her realise how close "the day" was. "It's only ten days and nine hours until your wedding."

But tonight her sister's voice sounded different, as if she had been crying.

"I shouldn't get too excited," Maggie said. "It might not happen any more."

Lucy stared at the lamplight from the street outside which shone through

Summer In Glen Clova

A SUNBEAM shone upon a distant ben,
The undulating road ran on and on,
I thought that Clova was the greenest glen
I'd ever gazed upon!

The pine-patched braes seemed welcoming and bright,
As if refreshed by gentle summer showers,
Their crevices, a botanist's delight,
Might hide rare alpine flowers.

A fertile glen — small fields and flowering trees,
All overlooked by sun-kissed mountains high,
And mingled with its water melodies,
I heard the curlew's cry.

From Clova, stony hill tracks steeply climb,
And lead to Ballater and Royal Dee,
But that green glen in halcyon summertime,
Was magical to me.

— Brenda G. Macrow.

the window on to the ceiling. She stared and stared and found her cheeks were wet. Not wear that beautiful dress. Not taste the cake that would be waiting at the baker's. It couldn't be true!

BUT it was. The next morning at breakfast, she played with her cornflakes and listened to her sister talking to their mother. It was something about an argument with Mike.

"He won't see sense," Maggie was saying. "He wants everything his way," she argued. "I said maybe we should call it off."

And then her mother said, "You don't mean that, Maggie." She poured tea from the dumpy brown pot. "He's such a nice man. I think you're being a bit drastic, dear."

"Please, Mum, don't go on about it. I feel bad enough as it is."

Lucy was horrified. It was like Christmas or a birthday not happening, only so much worse because this had never happened in her life before.

Her mother continued to talk in a soothing voice to her sister, but it only made things worse until Maggie jumped up from the table and ran out into the garden.

"Lucy, dear, go and see if she's all right, please."

Lucy hurried over the green lawn studded with daisies. Maggie stood by the lilac tree with its sweet scented blossom and all around her the garden was bursting into bloom and birdsong. Lucy moved towards her sister, afraid she would be angry and tell her to go away.

"Oh, Lucy!" Maggie took her hand and held it tight. They walked down a path where the garden sloped to a lower level and there was a valley fringed by ferns.

"What can I do?" She began to speak in the way Lucy liked, as if she were grown up and quite capable of understanding. "I love Mike, of course I do, but I'm proud. I can't go to him and say I'm sorry. I know I was wrong, too, but I can't do it."

* * * *

Later that day, Lucy opened the wardrobe and gazed for a long time at the pink dress hanging there. She felt she had never wanted anything quite as much as to wear it. There was only one thing to do: she would go and see Mike, even though the idea of knocking on the door of his big house and having to explain why she had come gave her butterflies in her tummy.

She waited for two days, crossing her fingers and hoping that somehow things would come right. Her mother looked sad and Maggie moped around the house.

On Saturday, Lucy made up her mind. Everyone was busy and didn't notice when she slipped out of the house and hurried along the street. It was a week before the wedding — warm, bright and sunny. She knew that Mike's family visited every Saturday so it was the worst day of the week for her to call, but she had no choice.

"My goodness, it's Lucy!" Mrs Hughes exclaimed as she opened the door.

Lucy swallowed hard.

"Please can I speak to Mike?" she blurted out.

"Mike?" Mrs Hughes sounded surprised.

"Yes, it's very important."

Mike's mother hesitated.

"He's not here at the moment, though he did say he wouldn't be long. Listen, we're just having tea. Why don't you come and have a bite to eat, dear?"

Lucy didn't know how to say no. She followed Mrs Hughes into the garden where everyone was lounging in deckchairs or sitting on the grass. As one they turned to stare and she felt her face redden. It seemed certain they all knew about the squabble between Mike and Maggie.

She bent her head to the glass of lemonade she now had, aware of the family furtively catching each other's eyes, wondering what all this was about.

Suddenly, she felt as though she couldn't stay. Lucy played her game: if Mike hasn't come home by the time I finish my drink, I'll go. But then she heard Mike's voice.

"I'm back." He came out into the garden.

"Look who's here, waiting for you," Mike's mother said.

There was an awful silence that seemed to go on for ever.

Holme Village, Yorkshire

THIS beautiful rural village is in West Yorkshire, close to the Derbyshire border, and enjoys a location on the edge of the Pennines, on the boundary of the Peak District National Park.

The water that makes its way off the surrounding moorland is the source of the River Holme, which flows down through the Holme Valley before meeting the River Colne at Huddersfield.

At last she gazed up at him. Slowly, he shook his head from side to side, murmuring her name.

"On your own?" He sounded disappointed. "Or did Maggie send you?"

"She doesn't know I'm here," Lucy muttered. "It was my idea." Suddenly, it seemed like a very bad idea and all she wanted to do was run away.

They were all staring at her again, waiting for her to speak, and her courage had vanished. If she didn't go right now, she would die, she was sure of it. Lucy slid off her chair and spoke very quickly.

"Please don't stop the wedding. I've never been a bridesmaid before and I've never ever eaten wedding cake." She could feel the tears pricking her eyes and rushed on. "And anyway, Maggie says she loves you and she's so sad all the time and I can't bear it any more."

It had all come out wrong, not how she had practised it at all. She had wanted to be grown up and say the things Maggie would have said.

Mike smiled and chucked her under the chin.

"Well, I'll be . . . all off your own bat, eh?"

Lucy's face burned as she glanced round desperately then dashed around the side of the house and out into the street. She began to run and did not stop until she was safely home.

"ARE you feeling OK, Lucy?" her mother asked. "You look a bit flushed. I think you'd better have an early night."

It felt cosy in bed, curled beneath the duvet with the night-light glimmering on the familiar shapes of furniture. On the verge of sleep she thought she heard the doorbell ring and footsteps cross the hall to answer it.

Next morning Maggie was singing in the bathroom. She came to sit on Lucy's bed and hugged her sister.

"Get up, lazybones, there's lots to do." Laughing at Lucy's puzzled face, she went on. "Oh, Lucy! Mike came here last night and he said he was sorry and I said I was sorry and then he kissed me and . . . oh, Lucy, there's going to be a wedding after all!"

* * * *

Standing behind the two figures in the country church, wearing her pink dress with rosebuds in her hair, Lucy felt very important, especially when the moment came to step forward and take Maggie's bouquet. She thought her sister looked like a princess with her veil thrown back, smiling as she cut the cake. Then Mike beckoned her to come and stand with them and he asked everyone to drink a special toast "to my diplomatic sister-in-law".

Everyone laughed and Lucy blushed. This time it was with happiness because, miraculously, everything had come right. She felt she would never be happier than on this day when she had been a bridesmaid for the first time. Burying her face in the bouquet, she smelled the sweet scent of June roses. ■

A Little Misunderstanding

by Nicola Geddes.

THE school bus growled off towards the village green and before it was out of sight, both Tom and Alice were falling through the door of the village store, calling to their grandmother.

"Hi, Gran!" The bell rang as she closed the door, and Alice dumped her bag and approached the counter.

Her grandmother turned over the account sheet she'd been studying.

"Hello, my dears. How was school?"

"Boring," Alice said. "Our maths teacher's got hairy ears!"

"Oh, you are tactless." Gran shook her head, but her eyes were smiling. "I hope you didn't say that in front of him."

Illustration by John Hancock.

Tom was eyeing up the ice-cream cabinet.

"You've got a new flavour, Gran — orange and mango."

"Thought I'd try it, see if it sells. No, Tom, put it back now, I'll send some up with your dad later and you can sample it at suppertime."

Tom closed the cabinet.

"There's a new boy in our class," Alice said, lifting the counter board and walking through. "He talks all la-di-dah and his dad's bought Evergreen Farm."

"I'm glad somebody has. Maybe that dump'll get sorted into a working farm again," Tom muttered, following her.

"This boy — William — says his dad's got big ideas for the farm. He's going to make a —"

"Campsite, among other things," Gran finished.

"Yes! How did you know?"

"The plans have been approved," Gran told them. "It'll be all up and running by next summer."

Alice didn't think the older woman looked very pleased about it.

"Won't it be a good thing? There'll be lots of new customers during the summer."

"He's opening a shop, too."

Alice and Tom looked at her. They knew, it having been talked about within the family from time to time, that the village store was always somewhere between "only-just-worth-running" and "unviable". Competition was not welcome.

LATER that evening, in their home just outside the village, the children were supposed to be doing their homework, but had been distracted. The empty tub of orange and mango ice-cream on the supper table had reminded them of Gran's shop.

"But it'll be great having another shop! Maybe they'll have decent stuff!"

"Tom, how can you say that? It'll be a rival for Gran. If there's a campsite, she ought to get the custom from the campers."

"She can still sell eggs from Mum's chickens and all the other supplies, like milk and baked beans."

"Campsite shops sell all that. And if the new place does loads of up-to-date souvenirs and things, Gran might lose out. It'd be awful if some rival knocked her out of business."

"It's good that there's another boy in the village, though." Tom quickly changed the subject. "I hope he's got a mountain bike. How come we've not seen him about?"

"He's duffed himself up somehow," Alice told her brother. "He's got his leg in plaster and he uses crutches."

* * * *

The new boy came into the village shop on Sunday morning after the early service. The bell over the door at the village store pinged and Alice, who was helping to unpack eggs into their boxes, smiled up at him.

"Hello, William," she said.

He was tall for twelve, pale, with dark hair that flopped over his eyes.

"Alice." He nodded at her, like a grown-up would. He sounded very pompous.

Alice wasn't very sure if she liked him or not.

He didn't say he wanted to buy anything, but stood there, balancing on his crutches, catching his breath.

"Have you done your English homework?" Alice asked, for something to say. "That essay about a local landmark? I did the abbey."

"Bit obvious," William said, glancing around.

Alice didn't think he looked impressed by what he saw, and she felt suddenly very defensive about Gran's choice of stock.

"I did the farm," he volunteered at last. He changed his weight, putting his plastered foot to the floor, wincing as he did so.

"Evergreen's not a landmark! All those falling-down gates and rusty, saggy barbed-wire fences. It's an absolute eyesore!"

"It won't be soon!" William flushed. "It'll be a real going concern when we've done it up. You just wait and see." His gaze wandered round the goods on the shelves and the old-fashioned counter.

This time it was Alice who went red. She knew Gran didn't really keep up with the times. The postcards weren't the panorama sort you got in bigger shops, and the souvenirs tended to be tea towels and slightly tacky mugs with views of the abbey. She wondered what the shop must look like to someone posh, like William.

"I'd like half a dozen eggs and a pint of milk, please," William said suddenly, and Alice turned to see her gran had come back to the counter.

Gran didn't notice the somewhat charged atmosphere, but put the milk and a carton of eggs into his jute carrier bag.

"Will you be all right with these?" She eyed William's crutches.

"I'll be fine, thanks. I'm going to ring my father to collect me in a bit." He gave her a lovely smile, nodded tightly to Alice, and left.

Gran thanked Alice for bringing down the eggs and tried to give her a bar of chocolate for her trouble, but Alice just hugged her and said no. She didn't want to eat her gran's meagre profits!

ALICE wandered down to the village green to see if her friend, Joanna, had been let out of her music lesson. And there, on the wooden seat that surrounded the big chestnut tree on the green, sat William, obviously waiting for his father. The sun filtered through the yellow-green canopy and he had lifted his plastered leg on to the bench and propped his crutches up against the tree.

"Alice!" he called to her.

She didn't really want to speak to him again, but he shifted his weight along to make space for her.

"Alice!" He waved and it would have been mean just to walk on by. She flicked back her long mousy hair and went over to him. He offered her a packet of mints.

"You didn't buy those at the village store," she said accusingly.

"I already had them," he said, taking one himself and persuading her to have one, too. She sat down.

"I did the Felon's Oak," he said, and when she stared at him, wondering what he was on about, he grinned.

"For English. That big oak tree on the main drive up to the farm. It's got quite a history."

"I remember — hangings and things. A horrid history! Is it haunted, do you think?"

"No such things as ghosts," William scoffed, and then added, seeing her frown, "Sorry. I do seem to be rather good at offending you."

"Perhaps I fly off the handle a bit quickly," Alice said gruffly. "Gran says I'm tactless, too." She smiled at him. She wanted to like this new boy and she felt sorry for him because of his leg.

"So — what happened?" She indicated the plaster cast.

"Fell off my mountain bike. Broke my ankle in about three places. I'll be out of it in a few weeks, though. I'm allowed to put a bit of weight on it now."

"My brother said he hoped you'd be a mountain biker! Tom Webber, in Mrs Norton's class. He's a year older than us."

"You were talking about me?"

"On Friday. We were . . . discussing the shop your father's opening when you've got the campsite running."

"Why?" William looked puzzled.

"Our gran runs the village store. She doesn't really need another shop opening right on her doorstep."

"Hardly on the doorstep — it's nearly two miles. I walked it this morning. I'm going to ring Dad to collect me, though. I can't face that trip back, even if it is easy on these lanes. And the visitors won't much like it, either."

"You walked all that way on crutches? Why didn't you just come down the back ride?" Alice stared at him as though he were crackers. "It comes out right opposite the village store, and it's less than half a mile from the farm."

William stared at her.

"You're joking! What ride?"

Alice turned round and pointed back up the road.

"It's really overgrown, so I suppose you wouldn't see it easily from the farmhouse. But that five-barred gate there leads on to an old overgrown ride that goes up through the woods at the back of your house."

"Wow! That's worth knowing!"

THERE was a small silence. Alice fiddled with her hair and cleared her throat.

"So, do you think it could make any difference?"

"To what?"

"This shop your dad's going to open. If it's not even half a mile as the crow flies from the campsite to the village store, couldn't your dad just get his visitors to come and buy their supplies from Gran?" Alice looked at him squarely and challengingly.

"I don't know . . ." William floundered and Alice took immediate offence.

"You think you're too good for the village, then? You think we're just a poxy village store?"

"Hello, Alice — got here as soon as I could." Joanna Reeves came hurrying up with her music case.

Kestrel

KESTRELS can be found in a variety of habitats — coastal dunes, moors, farmland and urban areas. You have no doubt seen one, as they are a familiar sight hovering beside a motorway or other main road. Glance up at a large tree or telegraph pole and you might see one looking down at you, scanning the area for prey.

The number of kestrels declined in the 1970s, probably as a result of changes in farming, and the bird was put on the Amber List. This is the list compiled by the RSPB in which red is the highest conservation priority, with amber the next most critical group and green the least critical.

Kestrels like to hunt by hovering at a height of approximately 50 ft over open country and swooping down on small mammals, lizards or large insects. The kestrel has perfected the art of stationary flight and looks to be almost effortlessly hanging in the sky, scanning the ground beneath it.

The kestrel will not build a nest of its own, but will steal one belonging to a crow or magpie, or make use of a church tower, old windmill or hollow tree.

The female kestrel is slightly larger than the male and both are brown coloured. The male, however, has a blue-grey head and tail.

Wildstock.

Alice was red in the face and furious. What a snobby, horrible boy he was! She flounced up off the seat and stalked away, dragging her friend with her.

She didn't look back, and missed the utter bewilderment on William's face.

WHEN Alice arrived home for lunch, she was horrified to find William sitting in her mother's kitchen, chattering away happily to Tom about mountain bikes. Her mother was organising lunch around them, laying the table and setting out glasses and a jug of water.

"Tom found your classmate stranded in the village, so he brought him back for lunch." She smiled at Alice. "When we rang his mum, she said it'd be nice for him to meet some of the villagers and would you and Tom like to go back with William this afternoon and have a look around Evergreen? Dad'll take you up. I must say it all sounds very impressive."

"Hmmph." Alice snorted, smarting afresh from what William had said earlier. But she was very curious, too, and agreed to go.

* * * *

After lunch, she and Tom piled into the back of the old pick-up and her father helped William into the front with his crutches. The two boys never stopped talking — suspension, gears, frames and tyres — and Alice caught her father's eye in the rear-view mirror. He winked at her and she felt better.

At least Tom had found a mountain biker friend at last — that was the only good thing she could think about William! She kept harking back to Gran and how some extra custom would have been such a boost . . .

"That's the Felon's Oak," William said suddenly, pointing to the huge old tree halfway along the private lane to Evergreen.

"Yes, William, we know," Alice said tartly. "We have lived here all our lives."

Her father frowned at her in the mirror.

"Sorry," she mumbled.

Moments later, she touched William's shoulder.

"See that gap in the trees on the lower woods there — that's the entrance to that ride I told you about, the one that shortcuts through to the village and comes out right opposite the Stores."

"Less than half a mile, you said." William turned back to Tom. "What do you reckon?"

"Yeah, tops."

"I'll tell my father. He'll be really interested. He'll want to clear it through and open the gate so our people can use it to get to the village shop."

"Thought you were having your own shop," Alice muttered.

"We are." William grinned suddenly. "But we're going to be mostly selling the things made in our workshops. And tools and books to do with crafts —

Mum and Dad are setting up a Traditional Crafts Holiday Centre at Evergreen. Our customers will live in wooden cabins called lodges and learn to do woodturning and carving, pottery, ceramics . . . all sorts, eventually.

"They'll be self-catering and the people will need to buy their supplies from somewhere. If your gran's shop is really so close by cutting out all those roads, we won't need to supply them with milk and things at all! Dad'll be so relieved to hear it, he and Mum were dreading having to run a grocery shop as well as the holidays."

ALICE slowly went very red.

"Oh," she said, staring out of the window at the green ride. "Oh. I see." She cleared her throat.

Her father looked at her in his rear-view mirror.

"You OK, Alice?"

Alice swallowed quickly and took a deep breath. She looked across at William and leaned forward to touch his shoulder again. It was a gentle, conciliatory touch.

"I think I've been a bit of a pig," she muttered, making a wry face. "I'm sorry. I got the wrong end of the stick, didn't I?"

"What stick, Alice?" Tom was watching her face. "You've gone puce."

"Shut up, Tom!" She elbowed him in the ribs, but with a bit of a grin now as she went on doggedly to William. "I thought your dad was trying to set up a rival shop to Gran's. I never thought a shop would sell anything other than things people in a village need for eating or cleaning or whatever. I'm sorry, William."

"That's OK," William said cheerfully. "I'm good at misunderstandings." He pointed to a large lump of hewn stone beside the drive as they approached the house. "That's one of my misunderstandings — I thought the building people had left that there, too close to the front door, so I helpfully rolled it down the hill out of the way."

"I sense a 'but' coming," Alice's father said, smiling as he brought the pick-up to a standstill in front of the newly renovated farmhouse frontage.

"Yes. It's a piece of artwork, apparently. One of Mum's arty friends gave it to her as a housewarming present." William looked sheepish and they all laughed out loud at his error of judgement.

"But secretly Dad was pleased I moved it, because he'd reversed into it about five times and dented his car."

They all laughed again as they got out on to the gravelled drive. Alice helped William get his crutches and his balance.

"I really am sorry," she muttered, and he chuckled again.

"It's cool, don't go on. Did your gran get the wrong idea, too?"

"Yeah. That's been hard for her. She loves her little shop."

"We all do," Tom said, overhearing and walking with them to the flagged front porch. "Hey — I've got an idea!"

At that moment, William's mother opened the huge oak door and Tom's idea got lost in the round of introductions and handshakes.

William's mother was tall and slim with her hair bound up in a brightly coloured silk scarf. She invited everyone in and within minutes a kettle was popped on to a renovated Aga and home-made cake was brought out and sliced up.

William's father and an uncle appeared wearing painting overalls and everyone sat down at the pine table, and a lively chatter filled the room.

And Alice recognised the wrapping on the big fruitcake and felt guilty all over again . . .

"You're just like us, only posher," she whispered to William, and he burst out laughing again.

"You do say the oddest things. Whatever's posh about us?"

"Alice gets these fixed ideas about things," Tom said, taking a big mouthful of cake. "She takes after Gran — oh, and talking of that . . ." He pulled out his mobile phone and stabbed in a series of numbers. "I thought we could all ring Gran and tell her about the shop right now."

"Let me tell her, Tom." Alice held out her hand for the phone.

HI, Gran, it's Alice. Guess where I am?" Alice felt her colour rising again as she remembered how hostile her gran had been about "the new people". She had to raise her voice over the din of everyone talking and laughing. "I'm at the farm — it's looking great! We're having a cup of tea and some cake — one of your cakes, Gran, from the shop! — and they're not having a grocery shop or anything like that!

"Gran, it's magic — they want to send all their visitors to your shop — theirs is going to be all full of crafts and equipment — and lots of people. Oh, Gran, it's going to be all right!"

At the other end of the line, her grandmother listened to the garbled excitement and allowed a wide smile to spread across her face. A ginger cat jumped on to her lap and settled down there, purring, sensing relief and peace and a great deal of love in the air.

And when the oh-so-very-welcome news was told and the phone call was over, the old lady, absently stroking him, found tears in her eyes. She remembered walking hand-in-hand with her late husband up the very ride that was going to be the link between the village and the new craft centre. In her mind's eye, she turned back with him to look at the Village Stores beyond the old wooden gate.

"We're saved," she said aloud, sighing. The cat purred harder and kneaded her lap with his paws, and she lifted him up and looked into his golden eyes.

"You hear that, Marmalade? Our little shop is going to be all right after all." ■

Dedicated To The One I Love

by Annie Harris.

HI, Liz. Just a quick e-mail from the hotel's computer, as I can see the rest of our group out waiting in the lobby already. India is amazing! Delhi was a fascinating blend of old and new. Arrived in Agra yesterday, and it's the big day today! No upset tummies, touch wood. Must be all the pills you made me bring!

I'm fine, sis, so please don't worry about me. And tell Mum and Dad not to, either. I feel really good. Oh, the tour guide's just arrived — a lovely young man, Anu — so I must go. Love to everybody, Laura xxxxxxxxxxxx

I snatched up my bag and hurried out to join the others queueing to board the minibus.

"Morning, everybody."

"Morning, Laura!" they all chorused.

"Another hot one," Robbie said. "Hope you've got your sunscreen, sunhat and sunglasses."

"Of course."

I smiled at them. I was so lucky — they were a really nice bunch, all so friendly, and we'd gelled together already. Five couples, one of them very young. On their honeymoon, Sandra had admitted, blushing, which had given me a bad moment. The rest were middle-aged, plus one solo man, Jimmy. He was fiftyish and quieter than the rest. Not unfriendly, just as if he preferred to be on his own. Well, so did I, for that matter.

Sudden tears sprang to my eyes and I hastily jammed on my sunglasses. I wasn't going to let today be spoiled. I wouldn't let it, I told my sore heart, and forced myself to concentrate on Anu's

Illustration by Mike Heslop.

commentary as we drove off.

Agra was the usual vibrant, colourful mix that we'd very quickly come to expect. Buses filled to overflowing, gaudily painted trucks, cars, motorbikes, rickshaws, bullock carts, even cows coming at us from every angle. And so noisy! Our driver joined in with the best of them, fighting his way through the mêlée, his horn constantly blaring.

The sun was already blazing down even though it was still early morning, and Anu hurried us to the entrance, where we stood in the shade while he bought our group tickets. As we moved forward I wondered if everyone else's heart was beating as fast as mine.

SUDDENLY, there it was — what my guidebook described as a poem in marble, a love song in white stone. I marvelled at how Shah Jehan, heartbroken after the death of his beloved Mumtaz, had devoted the rest of his life to creating a fitting tomb for his exquisite wife. The Taj Mahal, the most beautiful, most perfect building in the world.

We all stood, just gazing, until finally Jean, Robbie's wife, broke the silence.

"However many photos or TV programmes you see, nothing can prepare you for this."

She was right. It was sheer magic, so lovely that I caught my breath.

We followed Anu along the path by the water channel and up to a low platform where we gathered, laughing and joking, for the inevitable group photograph.

But then the photographer gestured us towards what Anu called "Diana's bench", and the moment I had dreaded had come.

A Japanese group were there already with another of the official photographers, each solemn-faced couple gazing in turn into the lens. Then they moved away, talking excitedly, and Jean and Robbie were quickly posed on the stone seat.

As Dick and Sandra, coyly smiling at each other, took their place, I saw that Jimmy, like me, was standing back, deliberately avoiding the photographer's eye. He was staring at the young couple with an expression of such deep sadness that I momentarily forgot my own churning emotions. Just for an instant I caught his gaze and we exchanged rueful smiles.

At last, the session was over and we were let off the leash to explore on our own. I was glad of that. I felt I needed to be alone to nurse a heart which, in this place where the sense of love was almost visible in the air, was so very sore, despite my brave words to Liz.

I wandered around until the heat and the crowds became overpowering, and decided to sit in the shade of one of the huge trees and just gaze my fill. As I walked along, looking for a free bench, I spotted Jimmy, also on his own, staring not at the Taj but at the ground.

I hesitated, then went up.

"Hello, Jimmy. Do you mind if I sit here a moment?"

He roused himself and smiled up at me.

"Of course not, Laura. Please, sit down."

"Thank you."

We sat in silence for quite a while, then I spoke.

"It's just so beautiful, isn't it? Like Jean said, nothing prepares you."

"And you feel that, if those four minarets weren't there to tether it to the earth, it would just float away into the stratosphere!"

I laughed.

"That's just what I was thinking myself."

He was silent again, then just as I was wondering whether I was intruding and should quietly get up, he smiled.

"I'm sorry, my dear. I'm afraid I'm not very sociable."

"Oh, don't worry —" I began, but he went on.

"I always knew today would be difficult, but I didn't realise quite how much. You see, Christine, my wife, always wanted to come here. It was her dream, and I promised her that, when I was retired, it would be our trip of a lifetime. I took early retirement last year but, almost at the same time, I lost her."

"I am so sorry." Impulsively, I put my hand on his.

"Of course, we knew her heart was playing up, but even so it was a terrible shock." He sighed. "So you see, Laura, it isn't altogether a happy day for me."

"It's a sort of, well, pilgrimage for you, isn't it?"

"Exactly. I've come for Christine."

"I'm sure she would be happy that you're here."

"Yes, she would. But what about you, my dear? You sometimes seem — I do hope you don't mind my saying this — a little bit down yourself."

"Oh, well . . ." I hesitated, then went on. "I was engaged, the wedding was fixed, and we were coming here on honeymoon. Then, the week before the big day, Darren decided marriage wasn't for him, after all. At least, not marriage to me," I added sadly.

"You poor girl." Now it was Jimmy's turn to pat my hand. "Still, as my Christine would have said — she was a very forthright lady — better to find out what sort of rat he was early than too late!"

I laughed in spite of myself.

"You're right, of course. And that's why I came here. I wanted to show him."

"Well, I hope he knows what an idiot he's been." Jimmy glanced at his watch. "I think we'd better be moving. Anu said two hours."

"Yes." Reluctantly, I got to my feet. "It's so hard to leave, though."

"Remember, we're coming back for the sunset. And that will be just as magical."

After that, it seemed natural for Jimmy and me to be together — at our second visit to the Taj, when it turned rosy-pink as we watched; in the restaurants; on the minibus; the hair-raising cycle rickshaw ride through the crowded streets of Jaipur; the elephant ride up to the Amber Fort, and finally on the flight home. By now I knew all about him: how he lived in Reading, had a son and daughter and two grandchildren, a boy and girl.

BACK at Heathrow, Jimmy's case came off the carousel quite quickly, but he insisted on waiting for mine. As we wheeled our bags out through Customs, he turned to me.

"I should have asked you before. How are you getting home? Is someone meeting you?"

"No, I'm catching the Heathrow Express to Paddington, then the train to Oxford." I looked at my watch. "In fact, if I hurry I'll catch the next one."

"Nonsense!" he said firmly. "It's much too late at night. My Nicky is meeting me — he can take you home once he's dropped me off."

"No, really!" I exclaimed. "I'll be fine, honestly. I'll give Liz, my sister, a ring on the train and she can meet me. She lives in Oxford as well."

"I won't hear of it."

Putting a hand on my arm, he steered me into the Arrivals Hall, where I was still protesting when a tall young man, a Jimmy thirty years younger with the same dark hair and pleasant face, appeared, and seized his father in a bearhug.

Nicky turned out to be just as determined as his father to get his own way.

"Rubbish. Oxford's no distance at all for me, and you can't go alone at this time of night."

So that was that, as they say. When we dropped Jimmy off at his home he kissed me on the cheek, and thanked me for all that I'd done for him. When I protested that he'd done just as much for me, he squeezed me in a bearhug.

Back in the car with Nicky, we got on really well, talking about India — which apparently was high on his own wish-list — until I yawned hugely and fell sound asleep, only waking as we neared the outskirts of Oxford.

Nicky's last words as he drove away were, "Remember, I'm under strict orders to pick you up next Sunday at two o'clock sharp. We daren't be late for Dad's very own holiday camcorder show!"

* * * *

Hi, Liz. Just a quick e-mail from the hotel's computer, as I can see the rest of our group waiting out in the lobby already. India's even more amazing the second time around. We arrived in Agra last night, and it's the big day today. Am really looking forward to showing off my Taj. It's a wonderful place for a honeymoon and I can't wait to be sitting on that bench.

Must go — the tour guide's just arrived and they're starting to board the bus. Love to Mum and Dad, Gerry and the twins, and yourself, of course.

And Nicky sends love to everyone, too. Laura xxxxxxxx ■

Safely Gathered In

I REMEMBER standing on tiptoe, in my maroon-coloured strap-and-button shoes, and pirouetting in front of the long mirror in Mam's bedroom. The long full skirt of my Sunday-best coat flared right out from my waist, showing the lacy tops of my new white socks. The coat was light brown, flecked with oatmeal, and had soft dark brown velvet material stitched to the collar and cuffs.

Mam said the design was called the princess style, after coats worn by the two Royal princesses. I wondered, as I gazed at my reflection, if perhaps I could be related to them, just a little bit.

"Margery! Get down these stairs this minute. We'll be late if you don't get a move on!"

Mam's shrill voice was enough to wake the dead, so Dad said.

I hung on to the banisters, swinging down the stairs two at a time so she didn't have to call again. I didn't fancy dead people wandering around our house.

Mam was pulling on her black gloves whilst sticking a dagger-like hatpin into her little round peacock-blue hat. Then, picking up her handbag and umbrella, she pushed Dad out through the back door.

I'd noticed she could do lots of things at the same time, but my dad couldn't. Once, when I questioned her about it, Mam had raised her eyebrows and said, "Well, 'e's a man, what do you expect?" Then she'd tut-tutted, which usually meant that she didn't expect a reply.

"Will you come on, our Margery! I won't tell you again!"

Propelled through the door by a sharp poke in the ribs, I joined Dad on our garden path, and we watched as Mam locked the door and hid the key under a brick by the drain.

Dad shivered, and tucked the ends of his woollen scarf deeper into the neckline of his gabardine mac. Looking up over our heads, he pointed.

"It's going to be fine tomorrow. See them mare's tails?"

Through the gathering dusk, the shapes of trees and houses around us were etched in shadowy outline. I peered up at the clear sky to see what he was showing me. A ray of setting sun was glinting over the horizon, shining through long wisps of white cloud spread out like the tails of galloping golden-red horses.

"Look, Mam — look."

I wanted to show Mam, but she hurried past, and we followed. It wouldn't do to be late for the harvest festival.

THE walk up through the wood to the church didn't take long. Mam and Dad didn't say much. I expect they were too puffed out with rushing. I know I was. I just hung on to Dad's arm and let him pull me up the hill.

It was quite dark when we got to the top, and millions of stars glittered in the sky like tiny candles lighting our way.

I remember that my ears were cold, and the frosty air made my nose run. I wiped it on the nice soft cuffs of my coat — on the underneath bit so it wouldn't show.

The figures of other people, families and lone walkers, came out of the darkness, joining together for the remainder of the walk to church.

"Evenin', Reg — evenin', missus."

Amongst the greetings, there was a hiss and a tug at my sleeve.

"Sit by me, Margy-bargy. I'll save you a seat upstairs." And Violet, my best friend, dashed off to bag seats with the clearest view.

A lantern was fixed up in the roof of the porch. Its yellow glow spilled down through the rafters, out on to the gravel and over the heads of people crowding around the entrance. I held on tightly to the belt of my dad's coat as we shuffled through the church door. I glimpsed thin, leafy branches of scented pine entwined with oak lining the stone walls. It was just like my den in the woods.

I knew I could have helped decorate the church! But when I'd asked the vicar's wife she'd looked down at me over her glasses and said, in that frosty

Kinfauns

THIS pretty little village lies at the western end of the Braes of the Carse in Perth and Kinross, about three miles east of Perth.

The ruined pre-Reformation church of Kinfauns dates from the fifteenth century, but its roots are older still — it stands on the site of a chapel of Scone Abbey that existed as early as 1226. The more modern parish church, pictured, dates from 1869 — the same year the "Friend" was first published! — and the Gothic Kinfauns Castle was designed in 1820-26 by Sir Robert Smirke for Francis, 14th Lord Gray.

way she had, "Oh, Margery, one doesn't really think one is old enough." Or something like that. Whatever she said, what she meant was "No".

As they entered the church all the men removed their trilbies and caps, while Mam and the other ladies patted their hats to make sure they were still in place.

Dad was making for a pew downstairs, towards the back, but when he felt me tugging at his belt he let me lead him up the curved wooden stairs to the balcony.

I could hear Mam behind us whispering, "What do you want to be going up there for?" and, "No thought for my legs!"

Mam's legs were legendary, so Dad said.

Violet waved a green prayer book frantically. She was sprawled over four spaces on the front bench. Her mother looked as if she was going to have a fit, her face was that red.

I sat next to Violet, then came Dad, then Mam. She couldn't say anything now, so she just pursed her lips for a bit.

VIOLET had kept the best seat, just as she'd promised. We leaned forward, elbows on the ledge, and peered right over the top and down on to everyone below.

Nearly every seat was taken. We watched as people fidgeted, taking off heavy coats and putting them underneath the pew in front. Handbags were

Gardener's Lament

THE weeds in my garden, they just grow and grow,
They do so much better than flowers I sow.
They bully petunias; the roses they mug,
Those nettles and bindweed — a mean bunch of thugs!
I've dug them all up, spending days on my knees,
They laughed at my efforts, and grew back with ease.
I sprayed all the dandelions — their leaves and their roots,
But the very next day, they sent up green shoots!
I'll give up the fight (and save money on seeds!)
Next year, I'll sit back and cultivate weeds!

— Antony Burr.

being opened, handkerchiefs brought out and tucked up sleeves, purses checked for loose change. No-one wanted to be seen lacking when the collection plate came round.

Coughing, desperately stifled behind outstretched hands, shoes scraping over wood block floor, falsetto whispers — all rose to where Violet and I sat taking it all in.

Then she nudged me, checking that our mams didn't see, and nodded in the direction of the door, where there were several rows of boys dressed alike in grey uniforms.

They were from the posh boarding school on the private estate down the road where Dad worked on the estate farm.

Their knees sticking out from short trousers gleamed white in the glow of candlelight. White and knobbly. Violet and I giggled like anything until everyone around us stood up, so we did, too.

The vicar, dressed in his white robes, walked down the aisle to the altar, followed by some more boys. These ones weren't showing their knees. They couldn't, for they were wearing long white dresses with frills round the neck. Violet and I were just about to fall about laughing when I thought better of it and glanced in Mam's direction. Sure enough, she had fixed me with one of her looks over the top of her reading specs.

I kicked Violet on the ankle, just to warn her. She shoved me back, and her mother reached over and clipped her round the ear. Luckily Violet's outraged yell was drowned out by the deep chords of the organ and the voices of the congregation as they joined together singing the first hymn.

Then the vicar stood up in the pulpit to talk to us all. I think he stood there to make himself look taller. He was only a little man.

"Knee-'igh to a grass'opper," my dad said.

Anyway, he went on a bit, so me and Violet passed the time looking round the church at the decorations.

There were lots of vases full of flowers. Great big chrysanthemums with sunshine-yellow faces stood stiffly to attention next to white spiky dahlias and sprays of raggedy-petalled purple Michaelmas daisies.

The stone window-ledges were piled high with apples, pears, cabbages, carrots, onions and big fat marrows like monster green and yellow striped caterpillars.

It was dark outside. The glass in the high windows looked black, like giants' eyes looking in at us.

I shivered a bit, then Violet pointed to a huge orange-coloured pumpkin. It filled the whole of the top of the font, where they usually wash babies.

"Our dad grew that," she whispered in my ear.

I felt a bit fed up because I couldn't see anything that I could lay claim to, and I didn't like Violet thinking she was better than me.

BUT then, as I searched, I saw it right at the front, in pride of place. I pointed, and hissed, "Our dad grew that."

A big golden sheaf of corn had had its stalks all plaited and made beautiful for the harvest festival. Ripe grain spilled out on to the dark red carpet.

"'E never!" Violet's disbelief was quite obvious.

"'E did." I was quite indignant. "'E ploughed the field, put the seed in, and drove the 'arvester the other day. I saw 'im. So there."

A loud "Shush!" from Mam stopped us in our tracks, and we passed the next few minutes trying to see who could pinch the other the hardest without making a sound.

There was a lot of kneeling down, then sitting, then standing up. Violet and I quite liked that. It reminded us of the Hokey Cokey, but the man who played the organ never played the right tune.

Dad handed me a hymn-book. He'd opened it at the last number shown on the board hanging on the wall at the front of the church. I watched, fascinated, as the organist straightened his shoulders, flung his head back, and with outstretched arms and splayed fingers, banged down on the organ keys with all his might.

As if on cue everyone stood and joined in together with the words of my favourite hymn.

"We plough the fields and scatter the good seed on the land."

They always sang my dad's song at harvest festivals.

After it had ended, Dad and I grinned at each other. I hugged his arm, and thought what a good job he'd done again this year.

Well, him and God. ■

Saving Gran's Tomatoes

by Gail Crane.

Illustration by Mandy Murray.

"TIMOTHY!" I really wish Mum wouldn't call me that. It's so embarrassing. I mean, Timothy might be an OK name for a grown-up, or a child, but I'm eleven years old and it's just so not cool. Suppose my mates heard!

I've almost finished mending the chain on my bike, then I'm going to meet Ryan and Max in the wood at the end of our lane. With all the rain we've had lately, the track we made will be good and muddy.

"Timothy!"

"Coming, Mum."

I'd better go and see what she wants before she calls again.

She's waiting at the back door and, from the way she's running her hands through her hair, I guess she's feeling really harassed about something.

"There you are," she says. "Grandma's just been on the phone. She says her wrist is really hurting her and she's worried about her vegetables."

About a week ago, Gran tripped over one of the canes she uses to stake her tomato plants and broke her wrist. She's back home now with her wrist in a pretty impressive plaster. She let Ryan and Max and me write our names on it in different coloured felt-tips. Gran's pretty cool for a grown-up. And she never, ever, calls me Timothy.

"Anyway," Mum goes on, "she's wondering if you would mind popping over and giving her a hand with one or two things. I said you'd love to."

"Oh, Mum, do I have to?"

Mum smiles.

"Just go and see what needs doing, then perhaps you can arrange to go back and do it another day. I'm sure your friends won't mind if you're a bit late."

I shrug and agree. It's no use arguing with Mum. She always wins in the end. Anyway, Gran wouldn't ask if she didn't really need help. She's not the sort to make a fuss about things. She's lived on her own now for years and does all her own gardening and jobs in the house — things that even Dad can't do.

But then, as Mum says, Dad isn't very practical. He doesn't like football or gardening or anything like that. He likes music and books. That's why I help Gran with the garden. I like digging and growing things. I like the cakes Gran bakes, too.

I don't really remember Grandad. Gran says he died when I was three. I know what he looked like because there are photos of him on the dresser. His name was Timothy, too.

Sometimes I wish Grandad was still alive. Ryan's grandad takes him fishing at weekends and Max's takes him to football matches. I'd really like that. I've asked Dad to go with me so many times, but he hates football and refuses to go.

I'll cycle to Gran's. It's quicker than walking, even though she only lives a couple of streets away.

GRAN is sitting in the kitchen when I get there. That's odd. Usually she comes out to meet me. She's looking pale and tired. She's looking older, too, but I guess that's because her wrist is hurting. I wish I could make it better for her.

"Thank you for coming over, Tim."

She gives me a quick kiss on my cheek and I look behind me quickly, hoping no-one has seen.

"I know you must have lots of things you'd rather be doing," she says.

"Not really."

Well, I can't hurt her feelings by saying I'd planned to go out.

"It's the tomato plants, you see. With all the rain we've had, they really need some stronger stakes. I never got round to finishing them properly after I fell and they are forecasting strong winds tonight. I'm afraid they will get blown down and we'll lose them all. So I was hoping you might help me."

"OK," I say. "Do you want to do it now?"

Gran and I have grown the tomatoes from seeds and it's been amazing watching them grow. There are loads of big green fruits on them now, so soon we'll be able to eat them.

"That would be wonderful, Tim. You're sure you don't mind? If you can drive in the stakes, I'll try and tie them up and, if we both do it, maybe it won't take too long."

It's hard work, pushing in the thick canes, and Gran's wrist is hurting her too much to tie the string, so she tells me what to do and I tie the plants to the new canes.

Then she asks me to pinch out the side shoots. We're always having to do that. Gran says they seem to grow new ones overnight.

"I'll come out tomorrow and do some weeding," she says when we've finished. "Otherwise, we soon won't be able to see the tomatoes for thistles and dandelions."

"I'll come and help you."

Have I really just said that?

Gran smiles.

"That's kind of you, but I'm sure I can manage to weed with one hand. You've worked hard this morning and I'm very grateful."

It's funny, but I've really enjoyed helping today. Gran couldn't have done it by herself, so I feel like I've really been needed and achieved something. I want to come back and help her again tomorrow.

"I'd like to," I tell her. "I've enjoyed it." And I really have.

* * * *

It rains a lot over the next few days, but Gran and I nip in and out of the garden between the showers. I weed the tomato-bed and pull up carrots, which I like eating, and cut runner beans, which I don't. But Gran makes me take loads home to Mum.

The tomatoes are swelling now and beginning to turn orange and the pumpkins, which Gran's growing for us to make Hallowe'en lanterns with, are getting fatter and yellower every day.

"It's all this rain," Gran says. "But we could do with some sunshine to dry things up a bit. Plants need warmth as well as water."

Then, one morning, Gran rings to say that there's something not right with her wrist and she has to go back into hospital for a day or two.

Mum says she expects Gran has been overdoing things again. She's always saying things like that.

Gran wants to know if I will look after her garden. I tell her I'm not sure I know enough, but Gran says of course I do and that she has every faith in me. She knows her plants will be in safe hands. And, in any case, it will only be for a day or two at the most.

But three days later, Gran is still in the hospital. There's been no sun and it's done nothing but pour with rain. Still, when I get the chance I go every day and check the garden. It's a good job it's the school holidays.

SOMETHING terrible has happened. As soon as I look at Gran's vegetable plot I can see it. My stomach's churning something awful and I'm feeling really light-headed. I guess it's what Mum calls shock. What have I done? What haven't I done?

I close my eyes tight and take a deep breath. Maybe when I open my eyes again everything will be OK. I open my eyes. And it isn't. All Gran's tomato plants are dead.

My eyes are stinging and watering like mad. Must be something in the air. I wipe my sleeve across my face. I am not — absolutely not — crying. I'm not a kid. I'm eleven.

What I am going to do? The leaves are all wrinkled and droopy and feel dry when I touch them. Some of the fruit looks kind of bruised, too — like apples do when I've left them in my pocket too long.

I'll have to tell Mum. She'll know what to do. I don't know what Gran's going to say when she comes home. She's trusted me and I've really let her down.

I walk home slowly along the street, wheeling my bike. I'm not in a hurry to get there. Other people don't seem to have a problem. There's a garden I pass on the way to Gran's that's packed full of all sorts of vegetables and flowers. Gran would love it.

I stop when I reach it, and look over the wall. It's quite a high wall, so I lean my bike against it and heave myself up to get a better view.

There are carrots and beans and all the things Gran grows. There are all kinds of weird plants as well. I mean, who would want to eat those tall prickly things? Yuk. It'd be worse than eating spinach!

"And what are you up to, my lad?"

I nearly fall off the wall.

A man who's even older than Gran is standing behind me, and he doesn't look pleased. I think I'm in trouble. I drop to the ground.

"I'm only looking," I tell him.

"Oh, yes?" I don't think he believes me.

"Those vegetables look so good," I say. "I wish I could grow them as good as that."

He's not looking quite so cross now.

"Do a bit of gardening then, do you?" he asks.

I nod.

"I help my gran," I tell him, hoping it might show I hadn't meant any harm.

"Do you now? So you know a bit about growing things?"

Red Grouse

THE red grouse is a medium-sized bird with a plump body, short tail and slightly hook-tipped bill. It is reddish-brown in colour and its feet are covered in pale feathers. Living for the most part in Scotland or Ireland, the red grouse loves a heather moorland habitat and eats heather, seeds, berries and insects.

The birds begin to form pairs during the autumn and their nest is a shallow scrape which is lined with vegetation. Eggs are usually laid during April/May and hatch after nineteen to twenty-five days with the chicks ready to fly after thirteen days.

The red grouse has been hunted as game for many years and is shot in large numbers during the shooting season, which starts traditionally on August 12.

Numbers have declined in recent years and the red grouse is not as common as it once was. This is thought to be due to the loss of heather, the creation of new conifer plantations and a decline in the number of upland gamekeepers.

Wildstock.

"A bit."

He's stopped looking angry, so I ask him if this is his garden.

"It is."

Then I think perhaps this man, who is obviously a brilliant gardener, might know what to do about the tomatoes. So I ask him.

"Do you know how to grow tomatoes?"

"Tomatoes? I should say I do. Mind you, it's not been a good year for tomatoes."

"It hasn't?"

"Too much rain and not enough sun."

"That's what Gran said. She said they need warmth as well as water."

"Wise woman, your gran."

"I think our tomatoes are dead." There, I'd said it.

"Oh, dear. And what does your gran say?"

"She doesn't know yet. She's in hospital and when she comes out she's going to be really upset. And I don't know what I've done wrong."

"Why don't you tell me about it?" he says.

So I do. And he listens and nods and then says, "What do you say we both go and have a look at your gran's tomatoes? Things may not be as bad as you think."

I nearly say yes. Then I remember that it's late and Mum will be waiting for me.

"I'm supposed to be home for lunch," I explain. "Mum'll be wondering where I am."

"Well, you go and have your lunch and, if your mum says it's OK, come and see me this afternoon. Tell her you met Sam Gardner."

I can't help grinning at that. He's got to be kidding.

"You're joking?"

"Nope. That's my name, all right."

That makes me laugh. I say thanks and tell him I'll see him later, then I get on my bike and cycle home. I feel much better now I've told someone.

Mum isn't at all cross when I tell her.

"You've done your best," she says. "No-one can ask more than that. I'm sure Gran will understand."

I tell her about Sam Gardner and Mum says she's met him a few times at the post office, and that it will be fine for me to take him to look at the tomato plants.

AS soon as we've finished eating, I cycle over to Mr Gardner's. I take him through the back gate into Gran's garden and show him the tomatoes, which are looking even more sad and droopy than they did this morning.

"I see what you mean," he says. "You know what you've got here, don't you?"

"Dead tomatoes?" I say.

"Not quite."

Mr Gardner pulls out a bottle from one of the huge pockets in his jacket.

"Thanks to you noticing it so quickly, I think we might just be able to save them."

"Save them?" I can hardly believe it. "You mean they're not dead?"

"Nope. They're pretty sick, mind, but I reckon with a dose of this they might just pull through."

I try to read the label.

"Bor-dee-ucks? What's that?" I ask.

Mr Gardner laughs.

"That's Bordeaux Mixture," he says. "Your tomatoes have got a bad case of blight and this is just the stuff to cure it. But we have to move fast. We need to go over each plant and take off every single leaf that's been damaged. Then we check the fruit and do the same with that.

"Then we collect all the blighted bits and put them on the bonfire and spray the plants with this. Then we keep our fingers crossed."

"Do you think it'll work?"

Stripping off all the leaves seems a bit drastic to me.

"Faith, my boy; faith. We'll see soon enough. Now, let's get started."

The plants look pretty weird now. We've taken off most of their leaves but at least there're still plenty of fruits left on. The rubbish is on the bonfire and Mr Gardner has sprayed the plants.

"That should do the trick," he says, "but you must keep an eye on them, and if you see any sign of blight you take the infected bit off straight away.

"OK."

I just hope this is going to work. I really want Gran to come back to a good crop.

"And mind you let me know how they're doing," he adds.

"I don't suppose you could come and look at them tomorrow?" I ask. "Just to make sure everything's all right?"

"Sorry, Tim. Tomorrow's Saturday. I'll be off to the match."

"Football?" I ask

"What else?"

Mr Gardner likes football!

"But I'll come back and check on them on Sunday. How would that be?"

I say that will be great and hope he enjoys the match. I expect Max will be there with his grandad. I wish I was going.

* * * *

Gran's been home nearly a week. She says she feels fine and she's glad to be back. I told her all about the tomatoes and she said she couldn't have done better if she'd been here herself.

Guess what? She knows Mr Gardner! She says they went to school together and he was in the juniors while she was in the infants. The other day he came to check on the tomatoes, which are looking pretty OK, and he and Gran sat in the garden together and talked for ages. He came the next day, too. And the next.

He says he comes to keep an eye on the tomatoes, but I can do that. I reckon he just likes Gran's cooking, because he always stops for a slice of cake or some of her apple pie.

It's Friday and I'm at Gran's for tea. She's made fruit scones and a chocolate cake, and Mr Gardner's here as well. He's spooning Gran's home-made plum jam on to what must be at least his tenth scone and Gran is watching him with a big smile on her face.

She asks him if he would like to come round for lunch tomorrow but I know what the answer to that's going to be because tomorrow is Saturday.

"I'd love to, Ellie," he says, "but it's the big match tomorrow."

Gran smiles at him.

"Still football mad, are you?"

"Nothing to beat it," Mr Gardner says. "It's the best game there is."

"You bet," I mumble through a mouthful of scone.

"Are you going tomorrow, then?" he asks me.

I shake my head.

"Dad hates it, so he won't take me. And he won't let me go by myself."

Mr Gardner and Gran look at each other in the way grown-ups do when they know something you don't. Then Gran winks at me.

"Tell him, Sam."

Mr Gardner reaches in his pocket.

"I just happen to have —" he says, trying to look all innocent "— a spare ticket."

My heart jumps. I know what's coming.

"I was wondering, Tim," Mr Gardner goes on, "if you might know anyone who might have a use for it?"

I'm grinning stupidly. I can't help it.

"Yes, please."

I can't believe it. I'm finally getting taken to a football match!

Then I notice that Gran has her hand on Mr Gardner's knee and he has put his hand on top of hers. They are both looking pretty pleased with themselves.

"In that case," Gran says, "you can both come round for supper afterwards. And who knows, we might just have a couple of tomatoes ripe enough to go in a salad."

Mr Gardner says that would be lovely. I think it would be pretty cool, too. ■

Illustration by Helen Welsh.

The Game Of Life

by Linda Chloe Elmon.

THE dangling row of gleaming conkers brought back clear memories of twenty years ago and the determined look on my grandson Ben's face. He'd just turned ten, then, and was settling into his new school in Kent.

"We need some conkers, Gran," he'd announced after school that Friday.

"Do we?"

"Yes. It's all they think about doing at break. Justin Ogden has got a thirty-sixer. He's beaten everybody. He's the champion."

I have to admit to experiencing a time-travel moment. Conkers! I thought conkers had barely made it into the Seventies.

It was clear that Ben felt a certain amount of awe at someone owning a thirty-sixer.

Thinkstockphotos.

"When I beat him they'll all be wanting to challenge me. So we need conkers."

I nodded, not at all surprised by Ben's use of when, not if. He had inherited Scott's determination. But I supposed conkers was as good a way as any to make friends in a new school.

My son, Scott, and his wife, Jennie, had moved down from Aberdeen to Lendale in Kent. They both worked in Information Technology and had decided that taking jobs at the head office in London before Ben started secondary school would be better than leaving it later and disrupting his schooling when it really mattered.

I'd come down to Kent to take care of Ben while they were on a course in America.

"Well, we'd better plan a proper expedition for tomorrow to find the source of the brown gold that men call conkers."

"Yes!" Ben said, his vivid imagination always ready for adventure. "We need a map. A treasure map. Mum and Dad have lots of Ordnance Survey maps in the box." He scampered off.

I was always astonished at the things Ben could come up with but I doubted the map would show the location of horse chestnut trees. I would need to use my own initiative for that.

"Right you are," I called after him. "I'll nip to the corner shop for provisions. We'll need sandwiches, fresh fruit to beat the scurvy, and bottles of juice that explorers always take with them. And you'd better find your haversack and give your walking boots a proper polish. Polished boots always impress the natives in a strange country."

Autumn In Applecross

OUR road from Shieldaig climbed the stony brae,
Where signs of autumn's glory could be found,
And, like a narrow ribbon, wove its way
Along the coast above the Inner Sound.

We gazed on Raasay, with its flat-topped hill,
Our road was bare; the lapping waters shone.
We passed some old stone houses, built with skill —
The homes of hardy folks in days long-gone.

At Applecross the autumn hues were bright,
The village made us wish that we could stay:
A cosy inn; white houses bathed in light;
A view of Skye that took our breath away!

From Applecross, the Cattle Pass climbs high
And leaves the friendly village far below.
We touched the clouds, and saw a buzzard fly,
Through mountaintops already brushed with snow.

— Brenda G. Macrow.

I didn't really need to go down to the corner shop, since the larder and the fridge were always crammed, but I had no idea where I might find a conker tree and I knew that wandering round the footpaths without a destination in mind just wouldn't do.

I came out of the shop with my provisions and the valuable information about two conker trees on the edge of the cricket field at Pennyworth, which was an even smaller village than Lendale, two miles to the south.

I brought Ben by a roundabout trek along the fever-tree-flanked, snake-infested river and we cut our way through the rainforest jungle represented by brambly woodland paths.

We had immense fun. After great trials the two intrepid explorers finally arrived at their destination.

The two trees were magnificent and they had shed the spiky cases holding the shining brown nuts bursting from their fleshy white setting. The conkers had the deep polished look of well-kept furniture or glossy motorcar paintwork.

We gathered up a bagful and then paused in the shade of one of the huge trees to have our well-earned lunch.

IT wasn't until Sunday night when Ben was tucked up in bed and I saw the conkers that he'd threaded on old bootlaces ready for school playtime battles that I remembered my brother and his school conker exploits. I wondered why I hadn't thought about Ronnie earlier. I think it might have been the knotted bootlaces which reminded me of all the magical things which needed to be done to achieve the qualities of a winning conker such as young Justin Ogden's thirty-sixer.

I resurrected that very thought the next day when Ben came back from school looking dejected.

"I didn't even get to challenge Justin Ogden," he said indignantly. "All my conkers were beaten by other people before I got a chance. They were too soft."

"Ah." I nodded knowingly and then explained about my brother Ronnie's conker rites involving pickling in vinegar, baking in the oven, rubbing with various things like boot dubbin and making sure you bored the hole through the middle in the right way.

We had a merry evening doctoring a dozen conkers until some had skin that looked like wrinkled old gnomes' faces. Ben went to it with a will. His energy and determination were boundless when he was given a challenge.

On Wednesday after school Ben was triumphant.

"I bashed my way to be a contender," he announced with glee, swinging a leathery looking conker round on its bootlace. "This is Robert the Brute, my twelver."

I got a blow-by-blow account of how he had decimated the opposition, and even better, I heard how he had advised his new playmates on conker preparation.

He seemed to have made friends already. Playtimes and lunchtimes were exclusively employed in spectating and participating in the conker challenges.

That night he polished Robert the Brute and placed the wrinkled shape on the bedside table. I sat having an evening cup of cocoa that night satisfied that his settling in at the new school was accomplished, and mostly by his own efforts.

THE next day he came back once more looking dejected.

"Where's Robert the Brute?" I said, although his face told me that I hadn't needed to ask.

"Leslie Barrett's got a real monster that beat everybody. No-one wanted to challenge it by the end of lunch break. Robert the Brute lasted two shots and nobody else did much better." There was disgust in his voice.

"We stood around talking for the last ten minutes. There was no-one left to challenge. Everyone wanted to know Leslie Barrett's secret. It's called the 'Nutcracker'. It didn't look as if it had been pickled or baked or anything. Of course, you're not allowed to have too close a look at someone else's conker."

I nodded as if I'd known the conker etiquette all along.

"Of course not. We'd better get out and find our own monster and give it the full treatment."

Ben brightened up at that, and after tea we set out for more conkers. We spent the evening doing all manner of weird things to our gatherings in an effort to make them impervious to Leslie Barrett's "monster". I drew the line at injecting Superglue, though.

* * * *

We needn't have bothered.

"Destroyed the lot," Ben said emphatically, flinging his arms wide as if to encompass every conker tree in Kent. "No-one even bothers counting now, not after it got to being a hundred-and-twenty-niner. Justin Ogden said it should be declared an unconquerable conker and retired for life with full honours."

"And what did Leslie Barrett say to that?"

"That the Nutcracker should be ceremonially planted behind the bikesheds. I have to help Leslie with the ceremony because my conker was the last victim of the Nutcracker."

Leslie Barrett sounded the kind of chap who was going to be a first-rate organiser.

"Leslie and I get on really well. I think I might be able to find out what the secret preparation is. Then I can have my own Nutcracker; only I'll call mine Conkrete."

ON Friday he said with a satisfied smile, "I think I'll be invited round to tea after school with Leslie one day next week, is that OK? The Barretts have got the baker's shop."

I nodded. I'd seen the quaint bow window of the shop with the name above.

"So, you think you might ferret out the secret of the Nutcracker, then?"

"Yup. It's really interesting talking to Leslie. The Barretts have lived here since Roman times." He looked thoughtful. "And besides, they probably have good cake left over from the shop like we used to get before we moved."

"I suppose your mum hasn't got time for baking now she has all that travelling to and from London to work.

"Why don't I bake a cake?" I suggested. "You can invite Leslie round here, then you're playing on home turf. And if the cake's really good, a slice to take home might do the trick. The Faulkners have a saying that good cake loosens tongues."

"You made that up," Ben said accusingly.

"Aye, but I'm a Faulkner so it must be true."

Ben couldn't find fault with that and so it was agreed. And I wanted to look at this Leslie. It was the first time I had ever heard Ben say that he enjoyed just talking to someone. He was a little dynamo and mere talking had always seemed a waste of time to him.

The hidden talents were totally unexpected. Leslie Barrett was a girl.

It was spelled Lesley; the wrong spelling had been in my head. For a second I must have stood open-mouthed, looking at the bright-eyed, dark-haired ten-year-old, and then I recovered and we went in for tea.

As I filled the pot I felt a deep sense of pleasure. Ben had said nothing about Lesley being female. I realised that he saw her only as a person. Considering Ben was so physical and rumbustiously boy-like, it was marvellous to feel he could view girls in this enlightened way. It seemed a great advance since my childhood.

BUT Lesley Barrett had a problem.

I wasn't aware of it when we sat down and made inroads into the Dundee cake I'd made. She was a very intelligent and thoughtful girl. She was almost totally opposite to Ben. She gave the feeling of calm strength while Ben's energy and power seemed all motion. Despite this they looked as if they understood each other well enough.

"I've been hearing all about your feats with your conker, Lesley."

She went pink, which surprised me since she looked so pretty and was so polite she must be used to getting compliments. And I was also impressed by the way she switched the subject of the conversation immediately and adroitly.

"Yes, but I'd rather be able to bake a cake like this. Everyone thinks that because my dad's a baker I should know things like that. Whenever Mrs Greenwood in Home Economics makes some comment to the class on baking she always says, 'Isn't that right, Lesley?' All I know about cakes is eating them, and this is great, Mrs Faulkner."

I really enjoyed the visit. I'm sure I didn't have half the poise or knowledge when I was her age that Lesley seemed to possess.

Immediately his tea and cake had disappeared Ben jumped up and wanted to show Lesley round the huge garden.

"Don't try to get Lesley to climb the apple tree. She's not dressed for it."

They were away for an hour and I was on the verge of going out and calling them in when they both appeared at the back door. Lesley was flushed but her eyes sparkled and she'd clearly had great fun. That was one thing about Ben: you never got bored in his company. You also got very little time for rest.

"We only came in because Lesley's got to be back. She does piano lessons."

"Well, you'd better walk her home then. But first of all, you'd better go upstairs and wash your knees. Look at that. You're not fit to accompany a lady."

Ben grinned.

Cardiff Bay, Cardiff

HISTORICALLY vital to Wales's economy by allowing the export of some 10,700,000 tons of coal from the Welsh valleys to the rest of the world each year, Cardiff Bay was previously known as Tiger Bay.

In 1987, the Cardiff Bay Development Corporation was set up to redevelop the area after it became very run-down when coal exports ceased in the 1960s. Nowadays, the whole area bustles with apartment buildings, water-based attractions including a wetland reserve and a sailing centre, and cafés, restaurants, bars and shops catering for all the family.

"Right. I'll only be a sec."

As soon as Ben was out of earshot, I heard about Lesley's problem.

"Mrs Faulkner, Ben's going to ask how I made the Nutcracker hard enough to win all the matches at conkers."

She pulled the Nutcracker from her blazer pocket and handed it to me. It was gorgeously brown, as if it had just come from its case.

It was plastic. A perfectly made replica, but plastic. You could only tell when you held it or peered closely at the hole, although that was mostly covered by the thick fluffy string.

"I had no chance of getting to talk to Ben, he was set on winning the conker championship. My uncle has a plastics factory which makes imitation trees, flowers and things like that. I sort of borrowed this so I could get to know Ben. He's so interesting; he loves adventures and history like I do. I didn't think that everyone would have to challenge me. It all got out of hand."

She smiled.

"Although I did get Ben's attention, didn't I? But what do I do now? Ben will know I've cheated, and I don't think he'll put up with cheats. I really haven't got a secret conker preparation."

I didn't have long to tell her. Ben wasn't the most conscientious of knee washers and he never did anything at half speed.

* * * *

"So how did it go with Lesley?" I asked when he got back. "She's a lovely girl, isn't she?"

"She doesn't know the preparation. Her uncle does the conkers. It's a family secret passed down for generations to the next in line. They have to take an oath never to reveal it. When her uncle dies she'll be next to learn the secret. But till then she said that we could try things together on our own conkers. Find our own secret recipe. She's got some great ideas."

I smiled. With her ideas and Ben's energy there wasn't much they wouldn't be able to do together.

"Well. That's good." I laughed. "Of course, if you marry her, then your son will be next in line for the secret and be school conker champion."

Ben laughed, too, at the outrageous idea.

"There's more important things than conkers, Gran."

* * * *

I smile now. I look at the uneven dangling row of burnished brown conkers strung across the pram to catch my great-grandson's attention as he lies kicking his feet with his father's energy.

I am guessing that it was my granddaughter-in-law Lesley's idea, and Ben did the stringing. ■

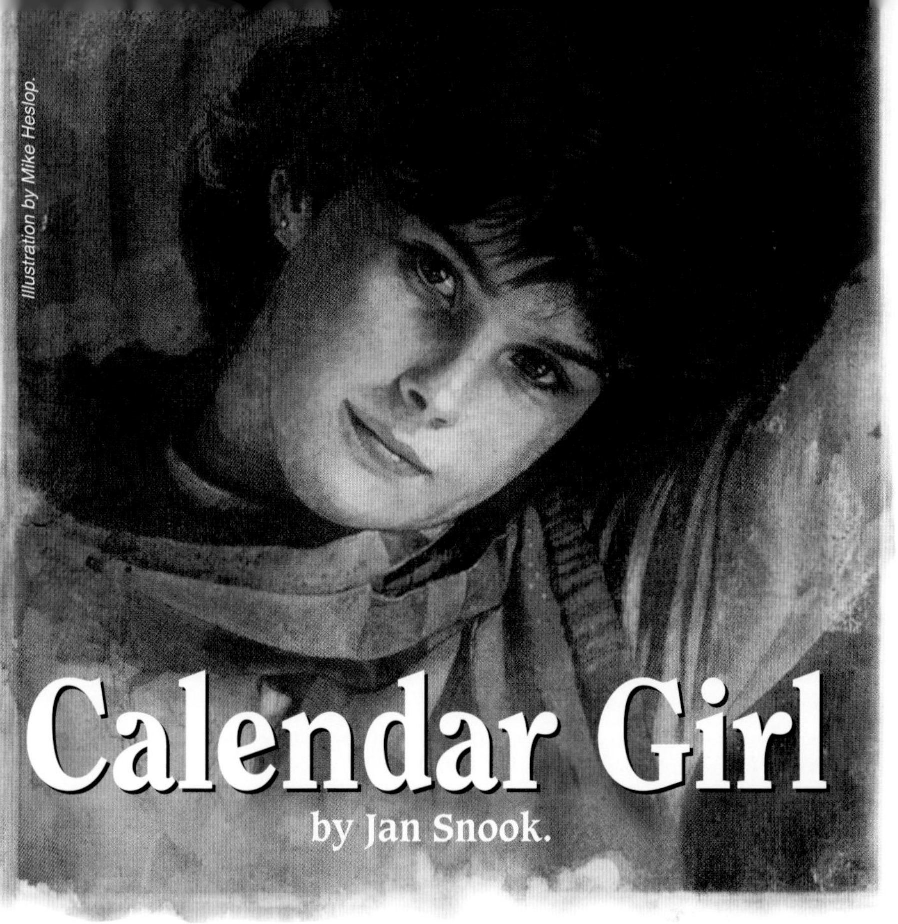

Illustration by Mike Heslop.

Calendar Girl

by Jan Snook.

THIS time, Gemma thought ruefully, as she splashed through the unseen muddy puddles in her wellies, her mother's matchmaking plans had gone seriously wrong.

Her mother's friend's son, Martin, was a killjoy and no mistake. He broke into her thoughts at that precise moment.

"And you say this happens every year?" He looked around incredulously at the hundreds of happy faces eerily lit by the flaming torches most people were carrying. "It's so . . . well, pagan. Not to mention wet and cold," he added, turning up the collar of his expensive designer jacket.

"Oh, dear, would you like to borrow this?" Gemma asked, beginning to unwind the beautifully cosy angora scarf her mother had knitted for her.

"No, thanks," he said a little too quickly with a fleeting look of horror.

"It's all right," Gemma persisted, laughing. "I know it's girly, but no-one can see in this light and it is bonfire night — people are dressed for warmth, not elegance!"

"So I see."

A couple of laughing teenage girls in fluorescent padded jackets had just passed them, their faces almost hidden by their scarves and hats.

They reached a slight rise on the way to the field where the fireworks were to take place and Gemma turned round to look behind them.

"Just look," she said breathlessly, taking Martin's arm and turning him gently. An endless snaking procession of torches wound its way behind them, strangely quiet under the dark, starless sky. "I come home for this every year. There's nothing like it in London. It's . . . magical."

"So why don't you live down here if you like country life so much?"

"There's not much work for a freelance photographer round here," Gemma replied a little wistfully. "And I like the buzz of London, too. You never know when you'll see something that will make a good picture. I never go anywhere without my camera."

"Except when it's damp, cloudy and dark, I presume."

"No exceptions," Gemma said happily, patting her pocket.

"When we eventually get to this field, is there any coffee or anything?"

"Oh, yes," Gemma answered, her mood of a few moments ago disappearing fast. "There are stalls selling coffee, soup, roasted chestnuts and things like that. And toffee apples and amazing hot chocolate," she added, the enthusiasm returning to her voice.

"Well, I suppose that's something." He hunched his shoulders and thrust his hands deeper into his pockets.

THEY arrived at the field just as the bonfire was being lit.

"Hi, Gemma," a friendly voice said.

Gemma recognised the man in the fire warden's tabard as a boy she had been at school with.

"You can throw your torch on to the fire now, but stay behind the ropes, won't you?" He gave Martin a grin, but Martin didn't respond. He handed the torch firmly to Gemma.

"You do it, if you must. I'm off to get a coffee."

Gemma opened her mouth to ask whether he would get her a hot chocolate, but he had already disappeared into the crowd. She turned towards the bonfire. Even from this distance she could feel the welcome warmth. She reached the ropes and threw her torch on to the fire, then turned away, forced back by the heat.

She looked around the field, wondering how she would ever find Martin again. There was a throng of people around the stalls, but she couldn't see him.

On the further side of the field, dark figures moved among shadowy structures that formed part of the firework display. It must be about to begin. Gemma felt the childish excitement rising within her once more. She turned towards the bonfire, and reached instinctively for her camera.

A small child sat on a man's shoulders, her pigtails sticking out from under her bobble-hat, a toffee apple in her hand. She was a perfect sharp black silhouette against the red-gold flames of the fire. Gemma's camera clicked at the same instant that the first rocket whooshed into the sky, filling it with light. As the sparks cleared, the child was still there, laughing with joy.

Gemma clicked again.

"It'll never come out, not in this light. Fireworks never do." Martin held out a cardboard cup of hot chocolate for her.

Gemma took it in surprise, swallowing her irritation.

"It's beginning to rain," he said, holding out a hand, palm upwards, to check. "This really isn't my sort of thing. I'll see you around."

Gemma opened her mouth to speak, but another firework split the sky and when she looked back down, he was gone. She turned round to see where the toffee-eating child was. If it came out, the photo would make a perfect calendar shot for November. She ought to go and find the father in case it did. She would need his permission to use it, after all. But they'd vanished, too.

GEMMA stared at the screen of her laptop. The photo had captured the excitement and wonder of Guy Fawkes Night better than she had hoped. The sky was flecked with the dying sparks of the rocket, and the child's silhouette was as crisp as if she had been cut out of black paper.

Gemma gave a deep sigh.

"Surely you're not disappointed with that one," her mother said, coming in at that moment and looking over Gemma's shoulder. "It's wonderful. The very essence of November. Is it for that calendar commission you've been given? It's a gorgeous photograph."

"I know," Gemma said, still sounding despondent. "But I haven't a clue who they are. And I can't very well just go ahead and use it without their permission."

Her mother frowned, acknowledging the problem. She peered at the photo once again.

"Well, it must be someone from the village. No-one else comes to these things, but I really can't think who that could be. You haven't got enough of the father to recognise him."

They stood in silence for a moment, both thinking.

"I don't suppose you took any crowd scenes or anything, did you?" her mother continued. "Other shots that might have a more recognisable picture of them, I mean?"

Gemma shook her head sadly.

"I only took that one shot." She frowned again then fiddled with the computer. "Unless . . ."

She smiled suddenly as the first picture she had taken burst on to the screen. The child and the man were there again, the silhouette effect spoiled by the sudden rocket, which lit the whole scene. Both their faces were tilted upwards and this time they were surely recognisable.

Thinkstockphotos.

Bonfire Night

ALAS, alack, poor naughty Guy, they burn him every year.
And not one person in the crowd will shed a single tear.
The air will fizz and bang and flash with annual display,
And yet, I always hope for rain to wash it all away.

I don't want to be a killjoy; I don't begrudge the fun,
But could we change the emphasis, then let the party run?
They did have bonfires long ago, as wintertime drew nigh,
When the old folk hoped to bring the sun back to them, by and by.

Imagine fires of hopefulness, smoke rising like a prayer,
Praying for a world of peace, a world of loving care.
And pray the fires burn safely, have the loudest bangers banned —
We don't need the noise of warfare ringing loudly through our land.

You can always find me hiding, about this time of year,
Comforting my frightened pets, alleviating fear.
The best part of the night, I find, when all is said and done,
Is the rain-washed smell of gunpowder, when all the fires have gone.

— Betty Norton.

"Who are they?" Gemma looked at her mother expectantly, silently thinking how devastatingly handsome the man was. Her mother was right about one thing — all the good men had been snapped up.

"Do you know, I have absolutely no idea."

Gemma was just walking back to her mother's cottage the next morning, having shown the photo to the woman, as well as assorted customers, in the village shop without any joy, when she saw the paper boy approaching on his bike. He didn't look any older than twelve, although Gemma supposed he must be, and she hesitated before getting out the now rather tatty photo.

The boy scarcely slowed down, merely glancing at the piece of paper and sailing past her. She was putting it back in her bag when he looked back at her.

"Ivy Cottage," he called over his shoulder then pointed. "It's over there."

A woman about Gemma's age answered the door of Ivy Cottage, holding a little girl's hand. The child had pigtails, though no toffee apple this time, and the woman looked at least nine months pregnant.

Well, what had she expected? It was no good mooning over some man you had never even met, especially when he had a small child on his shoulders. For goodness' sake, pull yourself together, Gemma told herself.

The woman was looking at her expectantly. Gemma got out the photo, and started to explain. The little girl was staring at the photo, wide-eyed.

"It's me!" she exclaimed. "Me and Uncle Nick at the fireworks!"

Right on cue, the devastating Nick appeared behind the woman and child.

"Allie?" he asked the woman enquiringly.

"Uncle?" Gemma asked, before she could stop herself.

The man and woman both started talking at once.

"My brother, Nick, yes, he's just come to help out in case . . ."

"The hospital's such a long way, and if Allie . . ."

"My husband works shifts . . ."

"If the baby arrives in the middle of the night . . ."

"Someone will need to look after Daisy . . ."

Gemma was laughing.

"Of course," she said in relief.

Nick was regarding her with interest. His sister looked at them both and hustled a protesting Daisy away into the kitchen.

"Stay and have some coffee," Allie called.

And that had just been the beginning . . .

GEMMA turned over the pages of the newly printed calendar carefully, looking critically at the photographs. Perhaps she should have used a different lens for the March photo, and July would have been better from a slightly different angle.

She turned more pages. November, though, was perfect.

"Pleased with it?" Nick asked, taking the calendar from her and kissing her gently on her forehead.

"Most of it," Gemma answered seriously. "Bits of it could be better."

"I really pity the photographer on Saturday," Nick said, shaking his head and laughing. "You'd really rather do the job yourself, wouldn't you?"

Gemma smiled.

"Well, I probably will have a camera concealed about my person somewhere on the day," she teased. "But I've conceded defeat. Even I don't think I can be the official photographer at our own wedding."

And then she kissed him back. ■

An Unexpected Guest

by Christine McKerrell.

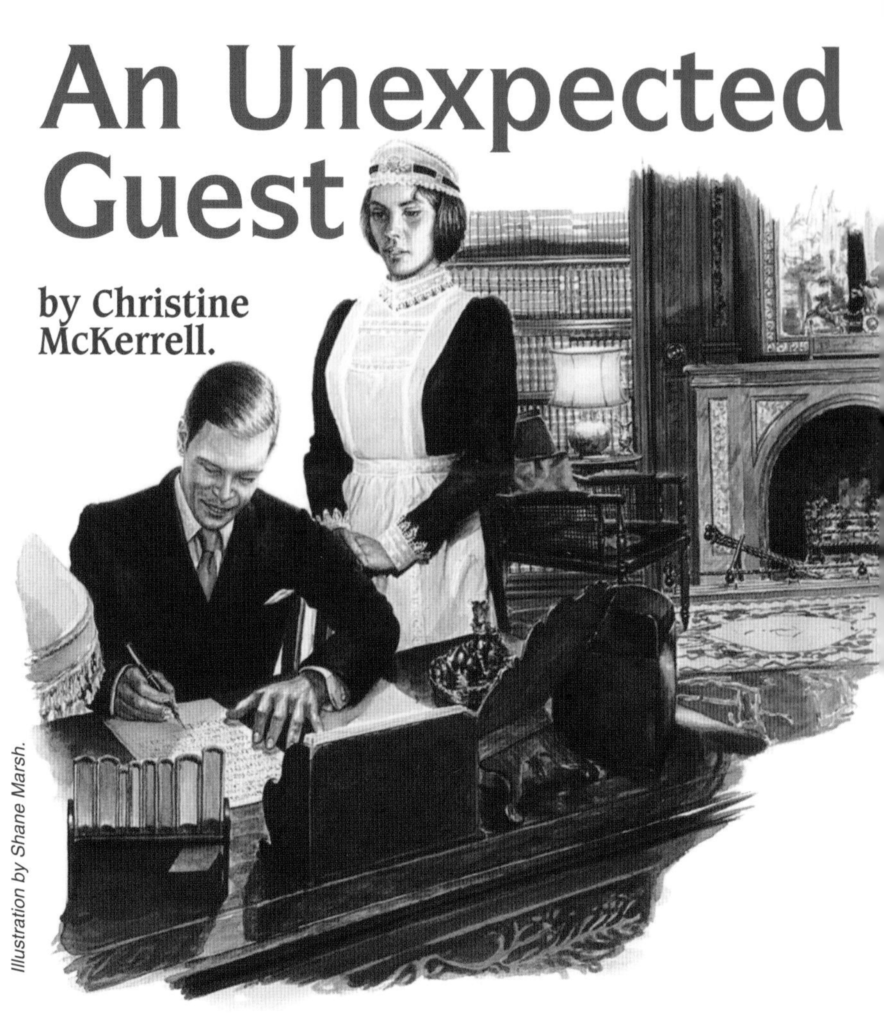

Illustration by Shane Marsh.

HUSH, Billy," Polly gently chided. "Mr Blackwood hasn't yet gone."

Her brother ceased the tattoo he was beating on the bowl and looked up, his eyes troubled.

"Is Mr Blackwood very ill-tempered?" he wondered, seeking his sister's reassurance.

Polly smiled and took the dish from him.

"No, of course not, silly. Hasn't he given Ma a job and let us live here?"

"It was Mrs Maggs that gave Ma the job," Billy returned, climbing down from the chair to pick up his sailboat, a cherished toy carved for him by their father.

"Now, don't you be running that thing along the floorboards," his sister warned.

"Mrs Maggs only got Ma the position on her word Mr Blackwood wouldn't be disturbed."

* * * *

"Elise Liddle's as good a soul as one could hope to meet, sir," Margaret Higginbottom had assured her employer. "And a hard worker, to boot."

Charles Blackwood had sighed and given careful consideration to the proposal.

"But two children, Mrs Higginbottom?" he'd queried. "I have every sympathy for the poor woman, losing her husband as she has, but I often work at home, as you know, and need absolute quiet."

The housekeeper nodded vigorously.

"That goes without saying, sir," she agreed, her honest face flushed with a determination to help an old friend in need. "But we are in want of a tweenie since that silly girl took herself off in a strop. I told her when she came that followers wouldn't be tolerated."

"Quite, Mrs Higginbottom."

Her employer raised a hand to stem the flow.

"Well, then," he continued in measured tones, "shall we say one month's trial?"

Though unmarried, Margaret Higginbottom's position in Charles Blackwood's household earned her the honorary status of "Mrs". Billy, unable to manage "Higginbottom", had immediately dubbed their saviour "Mrs Maggs".

In a previous situation, while head parlourmaid in a rather grander establishment than number twenty-two Elmwood Crescent, she'd taken the new maid, Elise, under her wing and the pair had become firm friends. When Elise left to marry a ship's carpenter by the name of Samuel Liddle, they'd lost touch until only a few weeks before. Overjoyed at the chance meeting in the little park at the end of the Crescent, they sat themselves down on a nearby bench where they could keep an eye on Billy as he ran hither and thither, scattering the piles of autumn leaves.

"And how have things gone with you, Elise, my dear?" Margaret asked her friend, noting the pale cheeks and the sorrow-filled eyes.

The younger woman bowed her head to hide tears that lately had flowed so easily.

"Oh, Margaret!" She sobbed. "Such terrible times . . ."

Little by little it all came out, how Samuel had gone missing, leaving his little family destitute. Margaret, good-hearted soul that she was, found herself promising to do what she could to help. And she'd been as good as her word.

"It's only the two small rooms," the housekeeper had apologised as she shepherded them up the narrow back staircase. "But comfortable enough, and way up here in the attic there's no danger of the little one disturbing the master with his play."

She'd fixed her gaze on Billy, hiding behind his mother's skirts.

"He doesn't yet attend school, I imagine?"

Elise Liddle placed an arm round her daughter's shoulders.

"Polly here will look after him, Margaret. Have no fear."

Polly Liddle glanced up with stricken eyes.

"But what about school, Ma . . .?" Her protest tailed off as her gaze met that of her mother.

Though bonnie still, her ma's face was drawn, her cheeks pale from the worry of finding herself turned out on to the streets with two children to care for. The girl managed a smile.

"Perhaps in a few months when Billy's of an age," she'd said hopefully.

"Perhaps," her mother agreed without conviction.

In a year her daughter would be twelve, old enough to seek employment of her own. Schooling was little use to her now.

THEY soon settled into life in the tall Victorian town house, falling quickly into the routines of Mr Blackwood's well-ordered establishment. At six in the morning, while the rest of the household slept on, Elise Liddle slipped from her bed and made her way down the back stairs that wound from attic to basement.

In the kitchen, the vast cast-iron stove had to be cleaned, the ashes sifted and fires kindled in the fireboxes. A tea tray was set for Mr Blackwood and a pot brewed for the cook, who must be called on the stroke of seven. Fires were lit around the house, and the table laid for breakfast.

As soon as Mr Blackwood was safely on his way to the city, Elise Liddle got out her brushes and dusters and set to with a will. In the afternoons, when Billy was laid down for his nap, Polly would tie an apron round her waist and lend a hand. Often, as she moved about the shadowy rooms, she sang softly to herself, songs learned from her father in happier days.

Though other houses at the far end of the crescent had succumbed to the new-fangled electric lights, number twenty-two had so far resisted its charms. Mr Blackwood, a bachelor of some independent means, considered gas light far kinder to his fine collection of paintings, *objets d'art* and intricately inlaid furniture. And then there was his collection of books. Leather bound, gold-tooled volumes stood in rows on shelves that reached from floor to ceiling.

Though forbidden by both her mother and Mrs Maggs to set one foot across the threshold, the temptation for Polly proved irresistible. In quiet moments, when Elise Liddle was occupied with mending and Mrs Maggs snoozed by the fire in her parlour, Polly would steal into Mr Blackwood's study.

* * * *

Amongst his friends, Charles Blackwood was known as a hospitable man. Many were the dinner parties held at twenty-two Elmwood Crescent. On the first occasion, Elise Liddle was called upon to help at table. She and Margaret sat in the housekeeper's parlour afterwards, reflecting on the events of the evening.

"He's a fine-looking man, is Mr Blackwood. Don't you think, Margaret?" Elise ventured.

"Indeed — and such a gentleman. You couldn't hope to find better."

"And Miss Marsh is very beautiful," Elise mused, speaking of a lady often present at these gatherings.

"Quite so," Margaret agreed. "I wonder at the master's not taking the plunge, so to speak."

"They are betrothed?" Elise asked.

The other woman waggled her head.

"An understanding, you might say."

Elise pursed her lips.

"That might upset your applecart," she said. "A new mistress and all."

But Margaret seemed unconcerned by the prospect.

"Not Miss Marsh — a real lady, she is. I've served under much worse, believe me!"

"Mind you, it's not every man who's suited to wedlock," Elise considered.

"Nor every woman," her friend put in. "Look at me."

"There's a lid for every pot!" Elise laughed.

The other woman dismissed the idea.

"Too late, I fear. Miss Marsh and I have much in common."

"How so?"

"Both working for a living."

"But she doesn't need to, surely? And what kind of work does a lady do?"

"Runs some sort of school. Not just for reading and writing, you understand. I believe there's a musical side to it, too."

ONE grey afternoon in December, when snow clouds hung heavy over the crescent and the lamplighters were making their rounds early, Polly set aside her duster and stood quite still, listening to the sounds of the house.

Her mother was in the linen room sorting through the sheets. Billy was asleep upstairs, while Mrs Maggs was sure to be snatching an hour by the fireside in her parlour. Polly gently eased open the door to the study and slipped inside. She needed no lamp to see by, since she knew the room all too well by now, and found her way readily in the gloom.

From a bookshelf she drew out a slim volume, one she'd been reading in snatched moments for the past week. As she opened it, a gentle cough and the rustle of a newspaper almost had the precious volume flying from her hands.

"A good choice," an amused voice told Polly, adding kindly, "and are you particularly fond of the Greek legends?"

All of a tremble at having been discovered, the girl dropped a swift curtsy.

Thinkstockphotos.

"I'm terribly sorry, Mr Blackwood, sir," she stammered, seeking to thrust the book back in its place on the shelf. "I thought you were out, sir," she managed, edging towards the door.

"Your name is Polly, I believe," the man said conversationally.

Polly bobbed her head by way of reply.

"Polly Liddle, sir." She risked a hasty glance. "Please don't tell Mrs Maggs, sir," she begged.

"Mrs Maggs?" The man looked puzzled momentarily then smiled. "Ah, you mean Mrs Higginbottom. Quite right to be concerned. Bit of a dragon, my housekeeper."

"Oh, no, sir," Polly protested. "Mrs Maggs is the kindest of souls. She found us a roof over our heads when the shipping company stopped Pa's wages and we'd no money to pay the rent."

She hesitated, fearing she'd said too much.

"Right again, Miss Polly." The man nodded. "I was teasing. Mrs Higginbottom is indeed a splendid woman." He paused, head on one side.

"Perhaps it's best if we say nothing."

Polly nodded vigorously.

"I won't come again," she promised. But Mr Blackwood shook his head.

"Nonsense, my dear. How can I deny a fellow enthusiast? You must come as often as your duties allow."

As Polly murmured her thanks, Charles Blackwood's expression grew thoughtful.

"Tell me, Polly," he asked, "is it you I hear singing about the house?"

The girl bit her lip.

"Oh, sir — have I disturbed you?"

"Not at all! Quite the contrary. I particularly liked your rendition of the old ballad . . . Now, what is it again? Pretty . . ."

"'Pretty Polly Oliver', sir," Polly broke in. "My father's favourite, too. He named me for it."

Charles Blackwood seemed to consider this.

"You say your father was a seaman?"

"Yes, sir. On the *Tamerlane*."

"And she went down?"

"No, but Pa wasn't on her when she sailed for home. The owners said he'd jumped ship."

"I see." The man was silent for a moment. "And where was this?"

IN winter's grip
We slide and slip,
As robins perch,
On logs of birch.
Carols sung,
And stockings hung,
With lamplight's glow
And mistletoe.
Wine is mulled,
The crackers pulled,
All is gay —
It's Christmas Day!

— *Brian H. Gent.*

Polly frowned.

"An island, Ma said. Malta, I think."

DECEMBER crept on apace. Snow pillowed the trees lining the crescent and the fir brought inside the week before Christmas was rimed with frost.

"The master's had it set up in the drawing-room," Margaret Higginbottom told the children, fixing Billy Liddle with a firm stare. "He and Miss Marsh have made a custom of decorating it together and we don't want anyone who shouldn't sneaking in there."

Billy's eyes shone.

"A Christmas tree," he breathed. "Pa brought us one from the market once."

Polly ruffled his hair.

"It was the very last of them. One that no-one else wanted, so Pa got it for a few pence," she whispered over his head and the housekeeper's expression softened.

"Well," she allowed, "maybe one little peek wouldn't do any harm."

The children's eyes widened at the sight of the splendid tree in all its magnificence. Shining glass balls in myriad colours jostled with hand-crafted toys. Strands of silver bells were strung row upon row and each branch was tipped with a tiny candle.

"Oh!" Billy cried, his eyes full of yearning.

Polly held tightly to his hand.

"Go on, Billy," she urged. "Which would you choose if you could have just one thing from the tree?"

The little boy's gaze darted from branch to branch, finally coming to rest on a tiny coach and four, its liveried coachman flourishing a whip to urge on his steeds.

"That one," he declared. "And you, Polly? What would you choose?"

His sister didn't hesitate. She had caught sight of the angel at the very top, with spun glass wings and a halo of stars shimmering in the firelight.

"I would have her," she told him and squeezed his hand. "Angels grant wishes, Billy. Make a wish on the Christmas angel . . ."

* * * *

Later that same afternoon, Elise Liddle found herself ushered into the study at the behest of her employer. She went with a heavy heart, sure she was about to be dismissed, but was met with a reassuring smile as Charles Blackwood bid her sit. Flustered and ill at ease, she perched on the very edge of the proffered chair.

"If it's about the children, sir," she began beseechingly, "if they've disturbed you in any way . . ."

Her employer shook his head.

"No, no, dear lady. It's not the children that concern me, but your husband."

Elise Liddle was silent for a moment, her bewilderment plain.

"Samuel?" she managed at length. "But he —"

"Disappeared while on shore leave? Yes, your daughter apprised me of the situation."

"Polly?"

Mr Blackwood gave a wry smile, gesturing at the bookshelves that lined his study.

"She and I share an interest," he told the bemused woman. "But to more pressing matters — your husband's ship was the *Tamerlane*, was it not?"

Elise nodded.

"And the company refused further payment of his wages?"

His voice softened as she bent her head to hide the glint of tears.

"It must have been very hard for you."

Elise's pretty face was a picture of despair.

"When you have children, sir . . ."

"Quite." Charles Blackwood paused, choosing his words carefully.

"I have, Mrs Liddle, a great many connections in the shipping world and have made enquiries. Now I don't want your hopes raised too high, but the second post has brought news — a letter from a detection agency. I employed them to seek information around the docks at Dover, the *Tamerlane*'s home port, I believe. By chance the ship had lately docked."

"And had they news of my Samuel?" Elise could scarce contain herself.

"There was a great reluctance amongst the crew to talk." Her employer grimaced. "But the prospect of a few shillings has a marvellous loosening effect on the tongue."

"They knew of his whereabouts?"

"It seems," Charles Blackwood continued, "there was a fight between two of the *Tamerlane*'s crew when the ship last visited Malta. Your husband sought to intervene and was cruelly injured in the attempt."

"Oh, sir, do not say he is —"

"Dead? No, no, dear woman. Not dead."

The report from the private investigators told a sorry tale, how the men involved thought that they had killed their shipmate and left him at the doors of a monastery. The ship was due to sail and must not be detained.

Charles Blackwood gave a wry grimace.

"Life is cheap, Mrs Liddle, time is not. The men would lose any bonus they might hope to receive if the ship were delayed."

"Then he is still on the island?"

"Indeed not. Once restored to health, the good brothers secured passage for him, realising he was English by his speech. He is in Dover."

Elise shook her head, not allowing herself to hope.

"It cannot be my Samuel. His faithful promise was that he would always return to us come what may."

Her employer nodded.

"As I'm sure he would, had he been in full possession of his senses. The crewman my man spoke to had seen Mr Liddle about the docks and, recognising his former shipmate, made a point of engaging him in conversation, soon realising he remembered nothing of the sorry business nor, indeed, his former life.

"Further enquiry revealed your husband to be residing at the seaman's mission and making some kind of a living offloading cargo and such like."

Elise rose abruptly.

"Oh, Mr Blackwood, sir! What must I do?"

"Nothing, my dear," he assured her. "With your permission I will arrange that your husband be brought here in the hopes that the sight of his family might bring him to himself. It may even be managed before Christmas."

There was a twinkle in his eye as he offered a handkerchief.

"I'm informed," he said, "that the gentleman has a very creditable voice."

AS Christmas approached, Charles Blackwood's dearest friends were summoned to dine. Afterwards the guests retired to the drawing-room, where a log fire blazed and the candles on the fir tree cast a golden light. Dressed in her best pinafore, hair brushed until it shone, Polly held tight to her mother's hand outside in the darkened hallway.

"Suppose they don't like me, Ma?" she whispered.

"Hush," Elise Liddle reassured her. "Of course they will. Mr Blackwood has himself heard you about the house. He asked specially and it's little enough we can do to thank him for all he's done."

Elise's tentative knock was answered at once.

"Mrs Liddle. Polly, my dear — come in, do. Don't be nervous," he whispered as he ushered them forward. "It's just a few old acquaintances. Miss Marsh you possibly know already." Dorothy Marsh smiled encouragement. "And, of course, there is our friend here by the fireside."

He raised a cautionary finger to his lips as he bade Elise take a chair.

Bearded and somewhat shabbily dressed, the man seemed out of place in such company, his face half hidden in shadow. Elise Liddle stifled a gasp, but did as she was bid, motioning Polly to stand by her.

"Dear Charles has told us that you sing, Polly," Dorothy Marsh said with a fond glance in his direction. "Will you sing for us now? Please say you will."

Polly smiled shyly.

"I'll sing 'Pretty Polly Oliver'," she declared. "It was my father's favourite."

She forgot her fear and the smiling faces of her audience, forgot all that had befallen them, her voice soaring pure and clear. As the myriad tiny candles on the tree cast flickering shadows about the room, the stranger by the fireside stirred. And then, while the assembled company held its breath, his voice rose in harmony with the child's. Polly faltered, her eyes widening at the sound.

"Is it my Poll?" the stranger called, half rising from his chair.

With a sudden joyful cry, Polly ran to him and threw her arms about him. Gazing beyond her, Samuel Liddle smiled and reached for his wife's hand.

"And my sweet Elise? Those aren't tears I see, my love? Ah, did I not say I would always come back?"

LYING awake in her attic bed next to her brother, Polly considered the day's events. Clasped in her father's arms, her joy had known no bounds. And then, when it seemed her cup was full to overflowing, Dorothy Marsh had beckoned her to the tree and bade her choose a gift.

Polly's gaze strayed to the angel, but she pointed instead to the tiny coach and four. Miss Marsh, however, had a keen eye. Little escaped her notice, and she insisted that Polly be allowed to take the angel for herself and pass on the toy she had so obviously requested just for the benefit of her brother.

Billy greeted the coach with almost as much pleasure as he had his father.

"My wish came true, Polly," he cried gleefully, running it up and down the rough floorboards until the flimsy wheels parted from the body.

The little boy's mouth immediately opened in a wail.

"Hush, now, Billy — you can look after mine instead," Polly told him.

Now, as she listened to her brother's gentle snores and glimpsed the precious angel held fast in his chubby fist, she felt a momentary pang for its loss that was only fleeting, and she smiled as she drifted into sleep. Pa was returned to them safe and sound. What more was there to wish for?

* * * *

"Well, did I exaggerate, Dolly?" Charles Blackwood had demanded when the door closed behind Polly and her parents.

Dorothy Marsh responded with a considered nod.

"You were not wrong, Charles. She has a splendid voice."

"So you will find a place for her in that school of yours?"

"She will have to study hard — and not only at her singing. How do you think she will take to that?"

Charles Blackwood dropped a fond kiss on her brow.

"I think she will take to it very well indeed!" ■

Illustration by Andre Leonard.

The Mistress Of Marbury

by Phillipa Kent.

YOU mean it?" Alicia said with delight.

"Darling Alicia, of course I do." Edward smiled down at her. "We have a September wedding as planned, after which I whisk you off on a six-month tour of Italy — what you've always wanted."

"Oh, wonderful!"

Stars shone in Alicia's eyes. How fortunate she was to have Edward.

Around them, the grounds of Marbury Hall were delicately laced with snow, and lights twinkled from the many windows of the great house.

Thinkstockphotos.

Proud to be mistress here since the death of her parents several years ago, Alicia had been in no great hurry to find a husband. But Fate had intervened. At the spring ball Alicia was introduced to Edward Mayhew. He was tall and handsome with a roguish twinkle in his dark eyes, and the attraction had been immediate.

For Edward, too, it turned out.

The alliance had much in its favour. The two famous names of Mayhew and Cressey would be joined, for Edward stood to inherit the family home and lands in the south, which meant that their time would be divided between the two great estates. More importantly to Alicia, this was a love match more than anyone could hope for.

A delicious little shiver touched her. Edward was immediately concerned.

"You are cold. What am I thinking of, keeping you out here without your cape?"

She took his proffered arm and allowed herself to be steered back towards the house.

"How pretty everywhere is. I do so love the first snow. It makes the house look so mysterious and magical. And there is nothing quite like a gallop on a snowy morning and going indoors to a roaring fire. Then there are the Christmas festivities to look forward to."

She sighed ecstatically.

"I doubt the outside staff would see it all in quite the same light," Edward said. "Though I do get your point. Would you prefer a Christmas wedding? It would make a splendid show."

"Defer our plans?" Alicia threw up her hands in dismay. "I think not. What of the guests? Think of the travelling and the state of the roads. And a full

Goodwill Bells

CHRISTMAS trees are covered
With a million twinkling lights,
This time of year serene and still,
With frost-sheened moonlit nights.
Wishes fly hither and yonder,
In cards red, green and gold,
Parcels and ribbons hold magic,
Reindeer sleighs bringing treasures untold.
Ice flakes are spiralling gently,
Upon us is Christmas Day cheer,
Rejoice in the carolling season,
As the goodwill bells ring clear.

— Dorothy McGregor.

twelvemonth from now is such a long time to wait."

"It is," Edward agreed. "Let's stay with our original plan, though it does mean you will miss your favourite time here, my sweet," he added with regret.

Tucking her arm more firmly in his, he escorted her into the house.

WITH Edward Mayhew being a regular visitor at the Hall of late, there had been much speculation below stairs as to what the outcome might be. So far nothing had been said. The only persons to get wind of the proposed union were Alicia's maid, Ellen Trews, and Edward's trusted manservant, Robins — and both were sworn to secrecy. The engagement was to be announced at the Christmas Eve ball, for which preparations were in hand.

"Three weeks to go," Ellen Trews said. She and Robins were enjoying a cup of tea in the servants' hall. She threw a cautious glance towards the kitchens, where Cook was chivvying the maids into getting a move on with the evening meal, and went on in lowered tones, "My mistress is ecstatic!"

"The master's the same." Robins helped himself to a slice of plum cake, Cook's speciality. "You'd think it had never happened before — which it hasn't for our master and mistress!"

Ellen Trews giggled. Neither servant was in the first flush of youth, but over the months a certain friendship had grown between them that made her feel a girl again and brought a spring to the manservant's step.

"The dressmaker was here yesterday with Madam's ball-gown. A picture she looks in it, too."

"She's a fine-looking young woman," Robins said. "Would you call her a good mistress?"

"The best. We're a devoted staff here and that always comes from the top. Otherwise, it's nothing but scowls and grumbles below stairs."

"True. Mark me, once they're wed there could be changes."

The maid looked up.

"What do you mean?"

Robins took a bite of cake, chewing thoughtfully.

"Well, Master Edward has got ideas ahead of his time and the old master is set in his ways. It's frustrating at Nethercote for my young master. I wouldn't be surprised if he doesn't put his new ideas into practice once he's in charge here."

"What sort of ideas? I know he likes his camera. Cook says he wants to take portraits of the staff and display them in the servants' hall."

"Master Edward always was one for gadgets as a boy. No, I was meaning more fundamental things. Like whether the wages are fair, or if the stable hands get enough time off."

Ellen Trews sniffed.

"He won't find any fault with the way Marbury is managed. Changes, indeed! The very idea!"

* * * *

In the library Alicia was pouring the tea.

"Have you ever thought," Edward said, eyeing the delicate bone china and gleaming silver on the tea tray, "how for the cost of that teapot you could replace the rotting thatch on the Home Farm cottages with roofs of good solid slate?"

Alicia stared, the item in question held high.

"But, Edward, the Marbury cottages have always been thatched. It's what distinguishes this estate from others — that and the black and white timbering. If the thatch is not in good repair then it is up to the bailiff to inform me, and then something can be done about it."

She put down the teapot, handing him his tea. Edward took it with a smile.

"And have you considered," he continued, "that for the cost of that entire tray of gewgaws, it may be possible to build a school at the village?"

"I wouldn't exactly put family china under the heading gewgaw," Alicia replied. "And why should the village require a school when it already has one?"

"Yes, run by the cleric at the vicarage. The pupils know how to recite their catechism and not much else. I'm talking about a proper school, where youngsters can learn to read and tot up a column of figures. Aye, and a smattering of Latin, too," he finished.

"Oh, surely not. These are village children. They need only to know the basics."

No sooner were the words out than Alicia felt a shadow from the past. Her mother had made the self-same remark when the present school was talked of. The project had gone ahead, with poor, dear Mama bewailing that no good would come of the poor attempting to ape their betters. Alicia had not been in total agreement with her parent, and now here she was reacting in much the same way.

"Alicia, I'm sure you can work that out for yourself," Edward said kindly.

Alicia tried to think how best to pursue the matter, but Edward's gaze was now roaming the tea tray.

"Ah, muffins! You remembered how much I like them. Thank you, my sweet. What a considerate wife I am to have, lucky fellow."

Somewhat mollified, Alicia passed him the muffin dish and helped herself to a slice of Cook's celebrated plum cake, while the fire crackled, dogs dozing before it, and beyond the window the short December day thickened to dusk.

THAT night, as Ellen Trews was brushing her mistress's hair before bed, the conversation at tea still rankled.

"Do you know, Trews," Alicia said. "Edward was talking about building a school for the children of the village. He also suggested replacing the thatch on the farm cottages with slate. He's never touched on these issues before."

"I had heard how Master Edward was very forward thinking, ma'am," the maid said carefully.

"Really?" Alicia regarded her through the looking-glass. Ellen Trews had put aside the hairbrush and was now deftly twisting the glossy chestnut-brown tresses into braids. "In what way, Trews?"

"I couldn't rightly say, ma'am. Although I expect when the time comes, the new master will be very conscientious over what's done here."

"How do you mean?"

"Well, ma'am, menfolk often have a knack of seeing what needs doing before a problem arises. Happen those cottage roofs may need some attention before long."

"But not at the expense of the family silver," Alicia said, more to herself.

"No, ma'am." Ellen Trews looked justly blank. She tied off the end of a braid with ribbon. "There, my lady. Will I fetch your hot chocolate?"

"Yes, do." Alicia yawned, patting her mouth delicately. "Dear me. All this tramping about in the snow has quite exhausted me."

Tired though Alicia was, sleep eluded her. She lay in the massive oak bed that had been made for a far earlier Cressey, the hangings drawn back, watching the flickering firelight on the ceiling and pondering.

Since she had been the only child of her mother and father's marriage, her papa had passed over the estate to her, so that Marbury would remain in the Cressey name even if she should marry. That much was legally binding.

As mistress of Marbury Hall she had managed the house and estate to the best of her ability. Her staff was well cared for, the books always tallied at the year end, and her dinner parties were the talk of all Staffordshire. Alicia had enjoyed her position of authority and it came as a shock to find herself open to question once she married. Men had a way of exerting their power, didn't they? So immersed had she been with this new and wonderful path her life had taken, she had barely given this a thought.

She slept at last, her doubts and uncertainties still simmering.

So next morning, Edward having suggested a ride around the estate, she was slightly on the defensive as they set off, their breath and that of the horses smoking in the frosty air. Edward had been a little late — which was unlike him — and Alicia detected an air of secrecy about him which puzzled her.

They trotted through the spinney and took the meadow path towards Home Farm, coming to the ubiquitous row of four timber-framed cottages. Reining in, Alicia cast her gaze over the roofs. True, the thatch did show signs of wear. One of the roofs must have sprung a leak in the wet autumn, for it had been patched with tarpaulin.

"I must speak with Anderson about that," she said. Anderson was the bailiff, a very busy man.

"Oh, I daresay it hasn't escaped the fellow's notice. Myself, I'm not one for thatch. It's a fire hazard, for one thing."

"But Edward, Marbury cottages have always been roofed this way."

"So you said, my love. It doesn't mean they can't be updated." His reasoning was totally feasible but Alicia, tired after the disturbed night and with that vague unease as to what the future might hold, felt a flare of pique.

"Reed thatch is known to be hard-wearing and warm. And it's a natural element."

"And slate isn't?"

Edward's smile was teasing, but to Alicia he sounded patronising and she flamed up all the more.

"Of course it is. That wasn't my argument. My papa was always adamant over refurbishment matters. He said if a material was adequate and serviceable it could not be bettered."

Edward looked rueful.

"Ah, Alicia. How many times have I heard that?"

"What do you mean?" she said sharply. "And please don't humour me, Edward. I'm not a child. If you have a grievance I must know about it."

"Call it, then, a difference in opinions between my father and myself. Papa, I fear, is sadly locked in the past. We beg to differ on many issues."

"You would make changes at Nethercote?"

"In some respects, yes. Keep the best of the old, by all means, but don't disregard the new. We have to move on, Alicia. There are exciting times ahead. I, for one, am glad to be part of it."

Alicia was silent. Change, to her way of thinking, was a strictly male prerogative. Let them dabble as they would, but someone still had to manage the household and organise the events that cropped up throughout the year.

"There are fewer than three weeks to go to the Christmas Eve ball," she said, suddenly remembering. The horses clopped on through the slushy snow.

"There are people here you have yet to meet. I thought of holding a dinner

Broughty Ferry

KNOWN as "the jewel in Dundee's crown", the Ferry lies four miles to the east of Dundee city centre. Its fine seafront esplanade and sweeping sands provide the perfect spot for getting out in the fresh air — for a bracing walk even if it's not picnic weather!

party beforehand and inviting them, so you won't feel a stranger in their midst."

"An excellent notion, my sweet."

"The invitations should go out soon. The week before Christmas might be best."

"Um . . . in fact, that may be difficult. Something has cropped up, Alicia. I need to go to London rather urgently. Business, you know."

"I see." Alicia's heart panged. Had she upset him so much that he wished to leave so unexpectedly? "In that case we had better leave it. Everyone will be at the ball. We can make the introductions then."

"That might be best," Edward said.

A WEEK later, he was gone.

She missed him. Edward had recently taken on much of the management of his father's business affairs and it was inevitable that he should be called away from time to time to the City, or to Manchester, where they had mills. These brief absences had previously added spice to the relationship. Alicia, occupied with the running of Marbury Hall, was happy to spend what spare time was left to her daydreaming about the future. And there was always the thrill of anticipation at Edward's return.

On this occasion it was not quite the same. That little altercation between them still stung. Alicia had brought up the matter of the cottage roofs with the bailiff and was assured that it was noted and repairs scheduled.

"The work cannot be done until the better weather, mistress. Meantime, we've done all we can to make the roofs watertight." The bailiff smiled, totally in control of the situation. "Now, ma'am, if you will excuse me I have to see the woodsman about the Yule log."

Anderson had doffed his cap politely and gone on his way, leaving Alicia biting her lip and vexed with herself. It had slipped her mind that thatching was a summer occupation, requiring the reed to be at its best and needing a fine, still day for the thatcher to work. One hint of a breeze and the reed blew away. Rain caused it to swell, with the result of a less tight fit. Too hot and the very opposite happened. It was what Bob Comely, the thatcher from Marbury village, termed "a right rascally business, and no mistake!"

Reminded of the merry-faced little man, Alicia's heart warmed. All the tradesmen and craftsmen who attended the Hall held a special place in her affections. She only hoped that Edward, when the time came, might feel the same.

In the next breath, she saw the whole silly situation through his eyes. No matter what the season, nor how inclement the weather, a roof of slate could always be laid. And whether thatch or slate, the inmates would anyway be every bit as comfortable.

Alicia heaved a sigh. There had been other signs, too, that made her fear that Edward had other things on his mind. The way he had taken to slipping off at odd intervals — walking the dogs, he had said. He'd never walked them before. He had closeted himself away in the library, too. Studying the layout of the estate, he had told her when questioned. But why? It seemed very odd to her.

The snow fell.

Alicia watched the twirl of flakes and thought of Edward. There had been no letter that morning, as she had hoped. Maybe tomorrow, she thought.

But at the breakfast table the following day all that lay beside her plate was the morning newspaper, carefully pressed as always. And there it stayed, unread and unwanted, while Alicia toyed with her food and ended up pushing the dish aside.

"It's been almost two weeks, Trews," she said afterwards to her maid. "He should be back by now. I do hope nothing is wrong."

"Happen Master Edward's stopped off to see his father?"

"I doubt it. He was intending to spend Christmas here at Marbury, and we were to go together to Nethercote for the New Year. Perhaps the snow has delayed him."

Perhaps she was being punished, a small voice within chimed. What did it matter who held the reins of Marbury Hall, provided the hand was steady?

"Try not to fret, mistress," the maid said. "There's time yet. Mark my words, Master Edward will be here for Christmas."

The days passed and still no word, and the festive event crept ever closer.

ALICIA liked to supervise the decorating of the house herself. First there was the Yule log to be brought into the main hall, with hot, spiced ale ready for the men who had the hauling of it. Boughs of holly and fir were cut to adorn the rooms, hall and great curved staircase, garlanded with bows of crimson ribbon. From the ceilings, circlets of mistletoe were hung to rotate gently in the draughts.

In the afternoon of Christmas Eve the carol singers came from the village, and were treated to hot punch and plum cake to fortify them during the cold trudge home. When evening came the candles were lit on the Christmas tree and the musicians took their place in the musicians' gallery, the tuning of fiddle and bass blending with the rattle of carriage wheels outside as the guests began to arrive.

This was Alicia's best-loved time. The great, glittering hall, the sparkling tree, the ladies in their bright muslins and silk and the men so debonair, the perfumes and tang of festive greenery, faintly laced with good cooking smells from the kitchens where Cook and her team were bent on making this the best event of all times.

It evoked in Alicia a sense of wonder and the knowledge that whatever might befall throughout the year, this very special season was here once

again to be revered and celebrated.

But on this occasion, as she made her tour of the rooms, the dogs padding along after her, Alicia's smile hid a heavy heart. For Edward still had not come.

"Something's sadly wrong," Cook said to Ellen Trews as she took a moment's respite from the steaming mayhem of the kitchen. "The mistress isn't herself. I was watching her during the carol singing. Her eyes were full up and that's not her at all."

"Christmas carols can be very poignant." Ellen Trews was not to be drawn.

Cook tried again.

"Seems to me this young gentleman is behind it all. He's been here on and off ever since the summer and very cosy it looked, too. So where is he now?"

"Called away on business," the maid said.

"Business?" Cook rolled her eyes. "We were expecting things of a more personal nature. I've gone through my recipes for wedding cakes. I've ordered the fruit."

A loud crash from the kitchens, echoed by a wail of dismay, had Cook winging back to her domain and Ellen Trews made her escape. Heading for the back stairs, she gave a woeful sigh. Before Edward Mayhew had left, Robins had confided that his master was off on a "special mission" and naturally the manservant would accompany him. Ellen, whilst not knowing what to make of it, had remained resolute that they would return. Suddenly, she felt a twinge of doubt.

She was about to ascend the stair when a voice hailed her.

"Ellen! Wait!"

Dreams

MOONLIGHT paints a silver path
Across the sleeping sea,
The stars look down from deepest heaven,
To watch o'er you and me.

Dreams are made in the silver night,
Before the flush of dawn.
Our spirits drift in time and space,
Till morningtime has come.

A soft wind soughs across the land,
And whispers by the shore,
Twinkling stars fade out of view,
And daytime reigns once more.

Bright daylight drives our dreams away,
Forgotten in the dawn,
And yet, and yet, before we wake,
Sweet memories linger on.

— Edward Mitchell.

She turned, and there was Robins coming towards her. His clothes were crumpled and travel-stained, his face strained with weariness. But he was smiling.

"You're back!" she cried gladly.

"Aye. We've ridden through blizzard and snowdrift to get here. There were times when I thought we'd never make it."

"We? The master's with you, then?"

"Yes, he's gone to see your mistress . . ."

"Oh, thank goodness. I'm glad you made it."

"So am I, my lass. So am I." Robins pushed a package into her hands and then held her gaze for a long, long moment. She felt her cheeks grow hot. "Will I see you later at the celebrations below stairs?"

"There's every chance." Ellen Trews gasped, and clasping the package to her, she turned and ran all the way up to her mistress's rooms.

* * * *

"Oh, Trews! Look!"

The package contained a book. It was no ordinary book. Inside the soft leather cover was page after page of photographs of Marbury Hall, all taken in the snow. Here was the house itself, roofs and pinnacles daintily iced. Here the spinney where Edward had proposed to her, there the farm cottages, their thatches dressed in white. The lake, the rose garden, even the stableyard, all wearing the wintry garb she loved and would miss the following year.

Everything slipped into place. Edward's mysterious absences when she had wondered where he could be. The suddenness of the unexplained trip away.

And she had thought it such nonsense!

"What a wonderful gift," she said mistily. "I shall treasure it always."

The maid, a new softness in her own eyes, was bustling about, spreading out her mistress's gown of white muslin over a rose-pink satin slip, fetching the matching gloves and slippers.

"High time you were getting ready, my lady. Will I ring for bath water?"

MUCH later, the dancing and feasting over, Alicia faced Edward across the hearth. In the great stone fireplace, the Yule log snapped and crackled. The dogs, having escaped from the library to which they had been banished for the duration, sat panting in its heat.

The speeches had been given, the all-important announcement made. Now, the last guest had gone, lamps were snuffed, the great hall was quiet and thrown into shadow. Around her neck Alicia wore the Nethercote emeralds, Edward's engagement gift to her. The gems flashed green in the firelight, but nothing could compare with the pleasure Alicia felt at that other present.

"Glad you approve," Edward said, giving her that special smile. "It was when you spoke of your regret at what you will be missing while we are in Italy. I thought I'd make some pictures, and then you can have them by you and look at them whenever you wish. The thing was, I had to go to London to get them mounted and bound. A deuce of a time it took as well. I was going to write, but I kept thinking it would soon be ready. Still, it's worked out in the end."

"Oh, Edward." Alicia's eyes brimmed. "It was such a beautiful thought. And I'm sorry about the roofs."

"Roofs?" He blinked, nonplussed. "Now you've lost me."

"The farm cottages? The out-moded thatch?"

Edward threw back his head and roared with laughter.

"Darling girl, 'twas but a suggestion, and not a very perceptive one at that. As you say, those pretty thatched bonnets are tradition here — but you must do what you will. You are mistress of Marbury and always will be."

"You . . . you mean it?"

"Of course I do. It was one of the first things I admired about you — that air of quiet authority. Would I dare to contest it?"

"Not even if I challenged the building of a village school?"

She looked at him askance, teasing, provocative, and Edward smiled again.

"Ah, there we may well have to come to an agreement. But I can be very persuasive."

"I think I've already found that out," Alicia said.

A hush fell, into which came the faintest drift of laughter from below stairs where the staff were still making merry. Beyond the windows the night was calm and clear. Edward took Alicia in his arms, holding her tenderly, and across the snowbound meadows sounded the first peal of church bells, heralding Christmas. ■

Red Deer

THE red deer is our largest land mammal. Its summer coat is reddish-brown, but its winter coat is brown or grey. There are no spots on the adult coat and it is only the stag which has antlers. The number of branches on antlers increases with age and some red deer can live up to eighteen years.

They are very adaptable as far as habitat is concerned, and can survive in woodlands and forests in England and southern Scotland as well as on open moor and hill in Scotland. They feed on grass and dwarf shrubs and will eat tree shoots in winter when other food is limited.

Grazing of tree shoots and agricultural crops puts many red deer in conflict with farmers and foresters due to the economic impact. Numbers are controlled by the traditional field sport of stalking, which brings valuable revenue to many rural areas.

The breeding season, or rut, takes place from the end of September to November. Stags compete for access to the hinds, female deer, by putting on elaborate displays. This posing and posturing can sometimes end in fighting, and serious injury and death can result from the damage a stag's antlers can inflict. The stag who wins, however, has exclusive mating rights with the hinds.

Wildstock.